If you are a parent whose child faces any ch a mental health issue or anything that take: column and places him or her in the "r you will easily relate to the messages in "typecast." Inside these pages are universal truths to inspire and strengthen us all.

—*Jacqueline Walters, parent*

Embrace this book! typecast is a collection of powerful stories of people showing us how to embrace type 1 diabetes, maintain hope and optimism, and excel in life. It is about a community sharing stories and helping others. It is a book about resilience and the people who exemplify that every day. For all these reasons, you need to read this book. Then, share your story because it is a story worth sharing.

—*Korey K. Hood, PhD*
Associate Professor and Licensed Psychologist
University of California San Francisco

Andrew Deutscher introduces us to individuals and families, including his own, who have learned diabetes is not an all or nothing condition. We can't pretend it isn't there, but it isn't all diabetes all the time. These stories remind us that success isn't just what you accomplish, but what you overcome. Each of us is defined by character, personality and heart, not a medical condition.

—*Gary Kleiman, Senior Director, Diabetes Research Institute*

This is a sensitive, engaging and intelligent book...zooming in on "attitude," the missing link to living well...and particularly living well with diabetes. It reinforces that family members, those with "Type Too" diabetes, are a powerful influence, also needing support and skills to be competent advocates and satisfied members of the family.

—*Dr. Wendy Satin Rapaport, Psychologist,*
Diabetes Research Institute

typecast

typecast

AMAZING PEOPLE OVERCOMING THE CHRONIC DISEASE OF TYPE 1 DIABETES

ANDREW DEUTSCHER

HUMBITION ENTERTAINMENT

Published by Humbition Entertainment.
Cover design by Base Art Co.
Interior design by Mi Ae Lipe, What Now Design.

Printed and bound in the United States
by www.BookPrinting.com.

To contact the author or order additional copies:
www.mytypecast.com
andrew@mytypecast.com

First Edition, January 2014
ISBN: 978-0-578-12311-0
Library of Congress: 2013950126

For my family, whose love and inspiration fueled this creation.

To my wife, Tara, Gavin's primary caretaker and my primary need.

To Jake, whose brand of patience and kindness in a diabetes household for an 8-year-old boy are beyond his years.

To Gavin, whose resilience, courage and joy for life play out every day he overcomes type 1 diabetes.

TABLE OF CONTENTS

ACKNOWLEDGMENTS

IF I HAD TRULY KNOWN HOW DIFFICULT WRITING A BOOK WOULD be, I'm not sure I would have embarked on this journey. What started out as a seed of an idea has blossomed into one of my proudest achievements. The experience has taught me at an even deeper level that anything is possible if you are committed and you have the right team around you. While I took on a great amount of work and played a variety of roles in bringing this book to fruition, it is profoundly clear to me that I could not have accomplished this without the support of many others.

My deepest gratitude goes to my wife, Tara, for supporting this project from the very beginning despite concerns about our privacy and bringing our story out to the world. That is not an easy thing to do, and I will be eternally grateful for her trust and willingness to put herself out there through my actions. While she provided emotional support, she also contributed in direct ways that have showed up in this book. Tara is by nature a very feeling and curious person. She asked questions about my contributors and had the wonderful suggestion for the foreword of my book. She has always truly taught me about love, and her support for the past two years has reminded me in specific ways how the people that mean the most to you can truly push you forward.

My two boys, Jake and Gavin, I couldn't be prouder of and happier about. I had to give up some Saturdays and evenings while I worked on this project at their sacrifice. I also recognize that I have been spending a great deal of time writing about one son's care, attention and experience. That has given me feelings of guilt around my other boy, a feeling I am afraid is all too common in the diabetes world where one sibling has type 1 and the other doesn't. The contributors to this book have taught me how to be more mindful of that and to recognize and deeply appreciate the challenges of the non-type 1 sibling. My gratitude, love and deep pride go to my two boys, both of whom support and love each other in such amazing ways, and their fire and passion make dealing with diabetes that much easier.

My mother, Alice, who has taken an active role in her area in addition to participating in our JDRF Walk each year. Her life-long encouragement and love has been a consistent source of fuel in my life.

With regard to the contents of this book, this would not be possible without amazing people. For the contributors of this book who represent so many others like them and inspire more to join the typecast movement, my deepest thanks go to Rob Campbell, Tom Karlya, Rich Hollenberg, Kelli Kuehne, Kamaal Washington, Jeff Hitchcock, Phil Southerland, Barbara Anderson, Morgan Patton and Derek Rowley.

Amy Campbell is a terrific content editor, and her skill in writing is only surpassed by what a great person she is. My sincere thanks go to Amy for turning my chapters into complete stories. I am so appreciative I had the privilege to work with such a pro.

On another recommendation from a contributor's friend, I have had the great pleasure of getting to know and work with Janet Cappiello, my copy editor. Janet's attention to detail and work on this project was like it was her very own. She stepped in as the project was nearing completion and I am amazed at how much she has built on it. I am deeply grateful for the expertise, responsiveness and care she gave this product to truly turn it into a book.

Mi Ae Lipe, who is not only responsible for the layout, but also was instrumental on all of the behind-the-scenes items to put a book together. Her attention to the book process and client responsiveness are deeply appreciated.

Dr. Avril Beckford, who contributed the foreword to my book, is our family pediatrician who quickly became our friend. With shared family experiences around type 1 diabetes, we are incredibly grateful to have Dr. Beckford in our life and in our kid's lives. When they don't listen to us, they listen to her. Along with Tara's ability to make anything taste good, she's the main reason our kids eat vegetables.

I also know this book would not be possible if I did not work for such an amazing leader and human being. Tony Schwartz, CEO and founder of The Energy Project, where I work as a senior facilitator and in business development, has changed my life in countless ways. He could not have been more supportive of this effort even though he had every reason to be concerned about the amount of time that could impact my work. Through Tony's own philosophies and strategies, he recognized that this project would fuel and inspire me to bring a greater amount of spiritual capacity to my work. I am fortunate to work for an employer who is so aligned with what he says and how he behaves. I know that has been a journey for him so I am proud through the completion of this book that this is yet another example of how he continues to free and fuel people by investing more in how to meet their four core needs; physical, emotional, mental and spiritual. Much of Tony's work and our collective work at The Energy Project is found in these pages, providing for a rich and detailed roadmap of how to live life at a higher level where renewal fuels health, relationships and human performance.

Many other friends, family members and colleagues were generous in sharing ideas, connections, providing feedback and overall support: Annie Perrin; Todd Henry; Phil and Bonnie Parker; Mike Kipniss; Trey Moore, Melissa Bauer and JDRF Georgia; Terry Rohrbach and Base Art Co.; Tate Lucas; Paula Ford-Martin; Matt Deutscher and family; Allan and Becky Deutscher; Steve and Jolene Gabbay; Michael and Pam Carroll; Jay McKenna; Gary Kleiman; Jo Southerland and Chris Fraker.

FOREWORD

IF YOU HAVE TYPE 1 DIABETES, HAVE A CHILD WITH TYPE 1 DIABETES or know anyone who has type 1 diabetes, I urge you to read this book. Worldwide, the incidence of type 1 diabetes is increasing each year by about 3%, and in North America by 5.4%. Researchers agree that this phenomenon is not explained by genetics only. This raises important questions for the medical community and community at large. We must find the triggers and we must find a cure, and until we do, we must do everything to support the children whose every moment of the day is impacted by this disease. Moreover, type 1 diabetes accounts for $14.9 billion in healthcare costs annually, and for all types of diabetes $245 billion, according to JDRF (Juvenile Diabetes Research Foundation). As a society, it benefits us all to pay attention.

typecast: Amazing People Overcoming the Chronic Disease of Type 1 Diabetes is a story of courage, compassion, struggle, turmoil and triumph. It's about the day in and day out of "hanging in there," while fervently hoping for a cure. It is a story of laughter and love, of reaching out and connecting as families and communities to tackle the challenge of living with type 1 diabetes.

Imagine a loving father and husband, in the midst of a busy and demanding world, having that world turned upside down in an instant—knowing that his son would never again have what most people regard as a "normal" carefree day. Little did 22-month old Gavin, a typical boy whose day was filled with running, jumping, playing and eating whatever and whenever he wanted, know that his life was to be changed forever on July 14, 2009. His days would now be filled with finger sticks, insulin injections and carbohydrate counting. His parents have always been fun-loving and relaxed. At the time of Gavin's diagnosis, life changed for the whole family: The days and nights would be punctuated by the ever-present question: "How is his blood sugar?" along with the ever-present task of managing a chronic disease for which there is as yet no cure.

When I met Andrew Deutscher and his wife, Tara, I didn't need to imagine. I've been there, as a mother of two extraordinary boys with type 1 diabetes and a pediatrician honored to serve the little people and offer support to their courageous parents, and my heart ached for them. It brought back the memory of being on an international flight from South Africa to visit our boys' grandparents. My husband (also a physician) and I were concerned that our 7-year-old, Justin, was going to the bathroom every 15 minutes, passing large volumes of urine and constantly trying to quench an unrelenting thirst. Our hearts ached; we knew what that meant. We went straight from the airport to Scottish Rite Children's Hospital and he was admitted with a diagnosis of type 1 diabetes. Then, at the age of 13, our younger son, Derek, called out to me. When I entered his room he was holding a urine dipstick in his hand and said "I have type 1 diabetes." He had diagnosed himself. He had been watching for the symptoms and checking proactively. We hugged. I cried. We knew that his life had changed. What I was to discover and hold in awe is the extraordinary resilience, character and courage that my sons and my patients with type 1 diabetes developed. Conquering this disease daily gives them maturity beyond their years and gives their parents a sense of courage and strength that is unique. As a mother and pediatrician, the diagnosis of type 1 diabetes changed my life forever. On one hand, it brought heartache to see the intrusion on my sons' lives, including the loss of my first born, Justin, who had a tendency to depression. With type 1 diabetes being an additional tipping point, he committed suicide on August 19, 2009, and I miss him every day, every moment. More than 75% of children with type 1 diabetes suffer from some sort of depression or anxiety at some time. On the other hand, it has enhanced my sense of awe and admiration for the courage, fortitude and wonder of children facing challenge.

Diabetes is more common than childhood cancer. Although we are fortunate that great progress has been made in treating and often curing childhood cancer, there is as yet no cure for type 1 diabetes, an autoimmune disease that requires hour-to-hour management and vigilance. The diabetes community still struggles with the lack of awareness and the confusion that surrounds the diagnosis. Many think that all diabetes is all the same, not realizing that type 1 is an autoimmune disorder and unrelated to lifestyle or diet.

This book finds the light in all of the challenge that any day brings. It is a story of resilience, of children having to be responsible beyond their years and parents finding the courage to let their hearts walk around out there on their own and empower their children to take charge and overcome. Remember the words in one of the stories you will read: "I have diabetes … it doesn't have me."

Avril Beckford, MD FAAP
Atlanta, Georgia
September, 2013

INTRODUCTION

A Problem Uncovered: Our Story

OUR STORY IS YOUR STORY. THE STORIES IN THIS BOOK ARE VARIED, yet they all tend to start out the same way. There is a common theme and overtone of a finality to a past life before you entered the new diabetes world. How did you find out? How did you know? What were the signs? How high was the blood sugar when you or your loved one was diagnosed with type 1?

In June of 2009, my wife, Tara, began to take notice of some unusual behavior from our 22-month-old, Gavin. "He just doesn't seem like himself," she would say. Most nights he was excessively wetting himself, had unquenchable thirst and he seemed unusually clingy and needy.

Living in the self-diagnosis era of Google and WebMD, Tara began doing some research. She also recalled, from great friends of ours, some symptoms of their daughter that were similar to our son's. She told me we needed to take him to the doctor and see if he had type 1 diabetes.

"Wow, wait a minute," I said. It was the middle of summer in Atlanta, so it made sense that Gavin would be thirsty, resulting in a lot of urination. I couldn't explain the behavioral changes, but I thought that was part of being 22 months old. We both agreed, though, that it made sense to have him checked. Since Tara is not a fan of taking her baby to the doctor in the superstitious hope that not going might make it better, I took him to our wonderful pediatrician, Dr. Avril Beckford.

Dr. Beckford is one of those magical people who you realize you are fortunate to meet regardless of what brings you together. When Tara and I first moved to the Smyrna area in Georgia after a job relocation, we inadvertently picked a fantastic location to be in Dr. Beckford's community.

Sharp, charming and full of energy and quick wit, Avril Beckford gives British charm a whole new meaning. The first time we met her about two years earlier during a regular checkup for our older son, I noticed how my mood shifted when she walked in the room. Not that I was in a bad mood, but we were there for a regular checkup for our son, not something in and of itself that puts you in an elated mood. Dressed in a corduroy blazer and jeans and with long, straight black hair, Dr. Beckford was as warm and friendly as she was confident. Her striking features are somehow further pronounced as soon as she opens her mouth and the British accent (only toned down mildly by her years in the States), fills the room. "Hello, hello. And, what is your name?" she said to our older son, Jake, as she put all of her energy and focus into him. You could see his expression change as she filled him up with positive emotion, and by the end of the session she said, "What lovely boys. I am so blessed and happy you are here today." In a world where doctors interrupt their patients, on average, every 18 seconds, the medical world could learn a great deal from how Dr. Beckford engages with her patients.

THE DAY OUR LIVES CHANGED

At our appointment with Gavin, the nurse came in and asked what the problem was. I explained everything and she said, "I'm sure he's fine. We have a lot of parents coming in this time of year with the same concerns." I was somewhat relieved, but would not be quite fully relieved until they tested Gavin. I liked the fact that the odds were on my side, but still had no proof he was OK. The nurse's assistant came in to take the first blood sample, pricked his finger and drew his blood onto a small strip inserted into a device to determine his blood sugar level. I felt this long pause of nervous anticipation. Never before had I experienced such a heavy feeling waiting for the five-second countdown to what my child's future would look like. A number came back: 527 mg/dl. Blood sugar is measured in milligrams per deciliter. The normal range is approximated to be between 80 and 120 most of the time. What did that mean? Well, by the look on her face, something not good. "Don't worry, I need to check again, it might have been an error," she said. I knew the chances of that being an error were not high, but I held out some hope. Second check: 565. OK, please stop doing that, I thought, he keeps going higher! "Be right back," she said.

Within a minute, a doctor who I had not yet met (Dr. Beckford was not in that day) came in the room and hurriedly explained to me what was happening. She didn't have much time, as she said I needed to get Gavin to the hospital right away. I remained calm, focused on the task at hand, while my insides were wrenching with a bad combination of fear, doubt and sadness. I raced home to give the bad news to my wife, who immediately started crying. "Let's stay focused right now," I said. We had to do what was needed for Gavin. There would be time to be sad and wonder "Why us?" but now was not it. We had to get him straight to the hospital.

Upon arriving at the hospital, the medical staff immediately took him into ICU and started treating his "high." That's what they call it when blood sugar is abnormally high. It's also called hyperglycemia. There was no doubt. Our son had type 1 diabetes.

The JDRF defines type 1 diabetes as "an autoimmune disease in which a person's pancreas stops producing insulin, a hormone that enables the body to move glucose contained in food and drink into cells throughout the body, which use it for energy. It occurs when the body's immune system attacks and destroys the insulin-producing cells in the pancreas, called beta cells."

JDRF says that the causes of type 1 diabetes are not entirely understood, but that "scientists believe that both genetic factors and environmental triggers are involved. Its onset has nothing to do with diet or lifestyle. There is nothing you can do to prevent (type 1 diabetes), and—at present—nothing you can do to get rid of it."

Left untreated, type 1 diabetes can result in blindness, kidney failure and death. Those with type 1 must monitor their blood sugar levels several times a day—mostly through finger pricks—and inject insulin to regulate the levels.

Type 1 is different from type 2 diabetes, also known as adult-onset diabetes, which is primarily a result of obesity. As many as three million Americans may have type 1 diabetes and each year, more than 15,000 children and 15,000 adults are diagnosed with type 1 diabetes in the U.S.

We were about to be thrown into a world we knew very little about with our hearts just aching for our baby. How long had Gavin had this? How long was he suffering? He couldn't tell us a thing. My wife had relied on her intuition to tell her that something was wrong. I still find it incredible that she had been so attuned to her son, but thanks to Tara's maternal instincts, she may have ended up saving his life. We were lucky, if you think about it that way. Our child would be fine. We just needed to reorient and learn a new way of life.

We were forced to change the channel. Sometimes change is thrust upon us and we deal with it. Sometimes it needs to be that way. When you are forced to change, you must find positive meaning in it. It may not be pleasant and it may not be what you were looking for, but it's here. You can let it keep you down, wallow in the "Why us?" syndrome, withdraw and complain, or you can embrace it, dominate it, learn all you can about it and move on. Here's the bottom line. Life will give you change whether you seek it or not. An unwillingness to change or adapt results in stagnation or simply being left behind. Gavin will never know what it's like to NOT have diabetes unless medical science presents a cure, and while we're hopeful, we can't control that. We *can* control the life we provide for him. As a result he will develop a strong sense of resiliency, fortitude and commitment. He'll be equipped to overcome obstacles and rise to occasions fueled by challenges and pain that help us grow.

EMBRACE IT

If you look at the actual etymology of the word "problem," you'll find that it is "something thrown forth." The prefix "pro" is to put forward, as in propel or progress. That being the case, why is a problem something that connotes difficulty or something that puts us into a negative state?

One thing we all have in common is that we have our share of problems. No question, some more than others. It seems that people with the most challenges or the greatest problems (loss of loved ones, health issues, financial setback) tend to view the world in terms of appreciation. There is of course that old saying that a problem is really an opportunity. So much of our emotion that is the filter in which we view our lives can be controlled or at least influenced by the meaning we give a situation.

Any great challenge, setback, disappointment or negative surprise in our lives comes with one essential question: How will you respond?

During those first few weeks after Gavin's diagnosis, as our new reality settled in and forever disconnected us from our former life, we made a decision to EMBRACE. I personally think about "embracing" as an actionable, committed word to taking control of your life and at the same time accessing and connecting to your new reality. Of course, there was sadness, anxiety, hurt, uncertainty and fear. Yet what we knew for sure was that we unconditionally loved our son and we were going to do everything in our power to help him, physically, emotionally and mentally.

Type 1 diabetes is a chronic condition that has far greater and wider implications than just the physical symptoms and manifestations. The emotional and mental well-being of a young child with diabetes is as crucial as an insulin shot and requires the same commitment to embracing his or her physical well-being.

What we have learned is that so much of diabetes care is about the meaning that you give it. The more you treat it as a chronic, debilitating, scary disease, the more your child or loved one will form his worldly belief systems around that. We have witnessed firsthand how powerful parental displays in the way diabetes is given shape in the home can be both good and bad.

On a bitter cold winter day, particularly for Atlanta, our family went to a large type 1 diabetes event to learn more about new technologies, hear the latest research and stay current on information.

At the beginning of the program, a parent got up to speak about what diabetes meant to him and how it impacted his family's life. He practically started the speech in tears and talked about their continuous state of worry and uncertainty, which led to more than 10 finger pricks a day, constantly questioning how their child looked or was feeling, their sleepless nights and fears of lows and highs, and ultimately, their greatest fear, losing their child.

As he cried during this talk, I empathized, sympathized and squirmed uncomfortably in my seat and looked at the more than 200 people in the audience, some of them newly diagnosed type 1, or new diabetes caretakers. I longed for them to hear the other side of the story, the story of optimism and inner strength.

The stories we tell are incredibly powerful because they shape our emotions, and our emotions influence how we actually experience our life. I firmly believe that despite this individual's best intentions to share experiences and the great love and concern for his child, he affected many people negatively. People are looking for hope, inspiration and a side of the story that can be empowering, uplifting and shape how you approach type 1 diabetes as a result of the meaning you give it.

REALISTIC OPTIMISM

The side of the story I was fortunate to hear early on was from one of my closest friends, whose daughter was diagnosed at the same age as Gavin, close to age 2. Steve Gabbay and his family have raised tens of thousands of dollars for diabetes research through personal contributions, generous friends and family. He and his wife, Jolene, also have a realistic optimism to their daughter's care.

It was in the early days of our son's diagnosis that Tara and I reached out to Steve and Jolene many times and felt their incredible support. Steve's outlook was similar to what I've come to really learn through my own work with Tony Schwartz, bestselling author and performance expert. It is an outlook called "Realistic Optimism." I've learned it is critical to having a healthy outlook for any conflict or negative stimulus, and I've found it especially helpful in managing the unpredictability and pressure of a chronic disease.

"Realistic Optimism," as defined by psychologist Sandra Schneider, is "accepting the reality of the current situation and finding a satisfying meaning therein."

In Daniel Gilbert's book, *Stumbling on Happiness*, he writes, "A healthy psychological immune system strikes a balance that allows us to feel good enough to cope with our situation, but bad enough to do something about it. What, then, might be a more nuanced perspective that includes both optimism and pessimism, positivity and negativity, without choosing up sides between them?"

Let's see what this looks like, and please go to **www.mytypecast. com** to add to either list or print out two copies and pass one along to a friend or family member.

I feel good enough to cope with this situation because:

- Type 1 diabetes is not a fatal diagnosis;
- Management of blood glucose is essential for everyone;
- I can form better behaviors early on that will become automatic and serve my health and effectiveness;
- I will learn about fierce intentionality and be more proactive;
- I or my loved one will be more resilient in the face of challenges;
- We're not alone. There is information and support everywhere;
- The recent advances in care and work toward a cure allow those with type 1 diabetes to live full and complete lives while giving great hope for an eventual cure;
- Bonding and community are an inherent part of type 1 diabetes;
- We have the power to choose how we respond to a type 1 diagnosis.

I feel bad enough to do something about it because:
- Type 1 is a condition that can have bad outcomes—loss of eyesight, kidney failure, etc.;
- I don't want my child to have to get shots and finger pricks each and every day;
- I want to have more freedom for all of us and not consider overall health on a constant basis;
- I don't want my loved one, or me, to feel different or less than an otherwise healthy individual.

In *Be Excellent at Anything*, Tony Schwartz writes: "If realism refers to the facts, optimism is the outgrowth of the story we tell about those facts."

FACING THE FACTS

Here are the facts:
- Type 1 diabetes is an immune disorder in which antibodies mistakenly attack healthy beta cells in the pancreas and disrupt them from the ability to produce insulin;
- Insulin is vital for our cells to absorb glucose, which is used to provide energy and sustain health;
- Without insulin, blood glucose levels would go too high, possibly leading to serious complications, as mentioned above;
- You need to regularly monitor blood sugar levels to determine how much, if any, insulin is needed to cover carbohydrate intake.

I've never seen *any* facts around diabetes that would make a person feel inadequate or that they can't accomplish everything they set out to. In fact, we have seen just the opposite with great people doing amazing things despite type 1 diabetes being a chronic condition to manage. It's those stories or the outgrowth of these facts that need to be shared, communicated and screamed about so we can truly see how insignificant type 1 diabetes becomes when we put it in the right framework.

It really comes back to embracing and actively participating in all you can do to stay positive in the midst of a situation that needs your attention. That's the simplest way I can break this down.

OUR NEW NORMAL

Our child is no different from any other who wants to love, learn, explore, play and grow. Watching Gavin run after ducks at the park, petting animals at the zoo or even wrestling me in his Power Rangers costume are universal rights! So, as a result, we don't treat him any differently and not everything is an emergency, and it's *never* an emergency as far as he knows. It's a new normal to abnormal circumstances, not one that we've chosen, but I truly feel fortunate because we can control it and my child can do whatever he dreams about and wants to achieve. That is a fact.

We may have a different language in our home with words like "glucose tablets," "highs," "lows," "insulin" and "basal," but in our home it's normal. You know when a child falls and you want to rush to them and ask if they're OK? It's interesting to notice that the less emotional you are about an event, the less likely they are to become emotional. Our energy feeds theirs and it's paramount that we're strong and in control so they can be, too. If you don't make it a big deal, they won't make it a big deal because your influence is so significant. In her wonderful book, *If You Want Your Child to Succeed, Let Them Fail*, Dr. Beckford makes the salient point that we need to be sensitive and aware to the over-cushioning of everyday impacts that can hurt a child's experience or growth. "Children need to be empowered to overcome the challenge that type 1 diabetes presents," she says. "We should nurture their ability to take charge of diabetes and live life to the fullest. In so doing, we help them develop the courage and resilience that is necessary for their success in life."

We diminish the type 1 impact at the same time we're dominating it. It's something to be dealt with to the best of our ability, not something to be controlled by and certainly not to be dictated by. And, most important, we are not going to let our actions be driven by fear. Our motto for Gavin: We got this.

YOU'LL BE FINE

Within a few weeks after Gavin's diagnosis, Tara was talking to one of her friends about the adjustments of providing, caring and managing a loved one with type 1 diabetes. Her friend said, "You know, Dr. Beckford has two sons with diabetes." Tara looked back in shock. Since Dr. Beckford was not at the office the day we took Gavin in, we realized that she probably had not heard the news yet. We immediately called the office and asked for some time with Dr. Beckford. She made room for us right away.

"How are you, today, beautiful boy?" she said to Gavin as his lips curled up. She just has a way of making kids melt in her hand. "Oh, I just love you and you are so brave," she continued.

Then, without missing a beat, she turned to Tara and asked her how she was doing. Tara half smiled and said, "I'm doing fine." In response, Dr. Beckford looked at her, held her hand and said, "No, you're not, but you will be. You will be."

A DIFFERENT SIDE OF DIABETES

The type 1 diabetes community is a strong, unified band of people who are entirely courageous and perpetually committed and hopeful. What we have learned as a family through our experience is that support is an amazing tool as you enter this community. While people deal with a diabetes diagnosis very differently, the type 1 community is empathetic, not just sympathetic to the plight. That makes all the difference because they literally have gone through the same trials and tribulations. They know the road because they've been down it.

My goal for this book is to convey that support and profile a different story of type 1 diabetes that we often don't get to see. It's the story of inspiration, hope, fortitude, growth and overcoming obstacles that every individual I spoke with and learned from genuinely feels. These values run through their blood and can easily be detected without a glucose meter. These are the stories that our type 1 children and all those impacted by the condition need to hear. Not only to understand empathy, but to experience this simple fact: *They are no different than anyone else.* They are unique to this world in their own special ways that have nothing to do with insulin, syringes or pumps. The stories in this book help us see that problems, setbacks, obstacles and challenges truly build our character, improve resilience, develop emotional fortitude, and, most important, help us live lives with fierce intentionality. In a fast-paced, complex world with infinite demand, these individuals find solace in planning, organizing, strategizing, creating and implementing what they want in order to be healthy, focused, committed and ultimately, happy.

In our society, we *typecast* people by making assumptions about what chronic illness means. We may view the diagnosis in a negative way: This person will be disadvantaged, limited by a "type" of lifestyle that requires restriction or a ceiling on potential. Through the stories in this book, you'll see that wherever you go, people are helping, people are contributing. There is optimism everywhere. People are discovering what they are truly capable of being. A type 1 diagnosis is not a limitation on your lifestyle. The inspiring and true stories that are happening every day and not limited by the confines of this book give us another viewpoint, a new *typecast*. The view that a type 1 diagnosis gives people the opportunity to become a different "type" of person—a courageous, motivated, disciplined, resilient and engaged person.

I am deeply moved by the power of story. These stories can be sad, cause anguish and make us cry. They also have the power to lift us, give us amazing perspective and serve to inspire. The power of story is just that. It's a perspective, a meaning, a way of looking at things. These stories and the stories we tell ourselves dramatically shape who we are and how we see the world. If emotions are how we experience the world, and I deeply believe they are, then the story creates the meaning that evokes the emotion. The people with whom I spoke and researched tell amazing and personal stories about what type 1 means to them. As a result, they fuel the right emotions to experience a joyful, optimistic and empowering version of the world. What an amazing lesson for all of us, but especially for our kids, to understand! It is the stories we tell ourselves that can overcome fear, displace doubt, fuel self-confidence and fortify resilience in the face of challenge. It's through the power of an empowering alternative story that new and improved typecasts evolve.

In writing this book, I have had the great joy of meeting, learning from and sharing how amazing people are not just living with type 1 diabetes, but thriving. You will meet:

- Phil Southerland, who was diagnosed at 8 months, one of the youngest diagnosed on record. His mother was told he could be dead by 25, most certainly blind. By 25, he was a professional cyclist, only blind to the riders behind him. He's now on a mission to put a team of type 1 cyclists into the Tour de France on the 100th anniversary of the invention of insulin (2021), while he tirelessly pursues insulin access for the developing world;

- Tom Karlya, who gave up a burgeoning acting career to take on the role of his lifetime as "Diabetes Dad," inspired by his daughter's diagnosis, and lives with great purpose and passion with no regret;

- Kamaal Washington, a teenager who couldn't find easy to understand information about his own disease so he created a comic book series to spread awareness about type 1 diabetes that gained national attention;

- Rich Hollenberg, a sportscaster diagnosed at age 35 who keeps his sharply upward career trajectory balanced with his family commitment;

- Kelli Kuhene, a former LPGA golfer who proudly sported her pump and mailed signed photos to type 1 kids while leveraging her celebrity and talent to raise money for diabetes causes;

- Rob Campbell, the humble and ambitious creator of the world's first tubeless insulin delivery system, an ever-forward person who has given back to the type 1 community in remarkable fashion;

- Derek Rowley, a young, bright and athletic world-changer who has set his sights high to innovate and drastically improve the business of medicine;

- Jeff Hitchcock, who started www.childrenwithdiabetes. com, a platform that barely stayed alive and is now flourishing with a commitment to stay true to its roots of helping type 1 families share, connect and find support in the midst of enormous growth;

- Morgan Patton, who with a skyrocketing A1C as a teenager found purpose and passion in sport and utilized it as the key to a remarkable turnaround in her own health, and continues to give back and change lives including those of rebellious kids who see themselves in her and what she has overcome, and;

- Dr. Barbara Anderson, whose care and commitment to type 1 families empowers us all to manage type 1 diabetes in our homes with less friction and more happiness.

These are great stories to tell. They are also an example, a representation of a myriad of type 1 individuals whose fire and drive are strengthened and fortified by having to face a chronic and challenging disease.

Let's embrace them, let's share them and most of all, let's lead by example. Anything can be accomplished and there are simply no reasons why a type 1 person can't grow and evolve into this *type* of person. What you'll also find—I hope—is that there isn't just one way of coping with this ~~disease~~ condition. Every story is unique, every story is important.

What's your story?

PHIL SOUTHERLAND

Cyclist, Activist, Author
Diagnosed in 1982 at age 7 months

Having type 1 diabetes united us, but it didn't define us.
—Phil Southerland, *Not Dead Yet*

IF YOU'RE TYPE 1 AND LIVE IN GEORGIA, YOU KNOW WHO PHIL Southerland is. If you're a bike racing fan, you know him. If you don't know who Phil Southerland is, then you have not quite experienced what inspiration and determination really look like, or fully appreciated what owning your circumstance is all about.

Let me introduce you to Phil and Team Novo Nordisk, formerly Team Type 1. The Race Across America (RAAM) is a 3,000-mile cross country race that is ranked as one of the toughest endurance challenges in the world. Phil's team of racers, all with type 1 diabetes, won this race back-to-back in 2006 and 2007, and a total of four times. It also holds the record for the fastest trans-continental crossing in just five days, nine hours and five minutes. It is mind-numbing when you really think about competing at that level of any sport with the added complexity of each team member managing their diabetes under extreme physical, emotional and mental pressure.

In 2008, Team Type 1 was unable to fill an entire roster of type 1 cyclists. Now, they're at 100% of type 1 cyclists and are expanding into other sports. The team boasts runners who compete in everything from 5Ks and marathons to full triathlons. There are 17 pro men, 15 pro women, 11 in development and 10 juniors. Add in more than 100 support people and now you have a system dedicated to transcending diabetes. Under Phil's leadership, the organization has grown from a cycling team to an enterprise, spanning the globe to inspire and unite people affected with diabetes. "Cycling remains the focus and the core," Phil says, "but what we've learned in cycling can be transferred to other sports." Their growth curve chart has been sharp and looks quite different than the tight blood glucose range of their athletes both in and out of competition.

"We were riding to make a statement on behalf of 1.5 million people who have a disease that's constantly in their lives, relentless, unceasing, and unforgiving, so how could we be anything but?" he writes in his book *Not Dead Yet*, his 2011 book about his life story.

"I am living proof that diabetes can be beaten into submission, which is what I'm doing every day of my life, and what I try to show others how to do."

—Phil Southerland, *Not Dead Yet*

In 1982, being diagnosed with type 1 diabetes was a lot more challenging than it is today, particularly at an early age. Phil, now 31, was lucky to have an incredibly devoted and tireless mother, Joanna, who knew that something was very wrong with her baby. At

7 months old, Phil was losing weight rapidly despite nursing all the time, and his diapers were always soaked.

Phil captures this moment precisely in *Not Dead Yet*. In spite of a young pediatrician's repeated assurances that nothing was wrong with her son, it took the most extreme of circumstances for her to recognize that he was in fact, dying. Looking back on it, Joanna recalls that the answers she was getting from the doctor were just not right. It was apparent that something was deeply wrong with her son, and it was more than just a frightened women's intuition that increased her resolve. The doctor's response, "He's probably teething," to Phil's excessive nursing, along with a lack of an explanation for his fruity-scented breath were enough to set off alarm bells for Joanna that she was just not getting the help she needed.

"One thing about me is I am not afraid to speak my mind," Joanna says. Speaking up saved her son's life and it's a reminder for all of us to stand up for what we believe in, regardless of our situation, whether it be to challenge a "more knowledgeable" doctor or to push someone for better answers. Joanna knew that if she did nothing, her life would be filled with regret, after losing her baby, for not speaking up and taking action.

DEFYING DEATH

The day Joanna Southerland took her baby to Tallahassee Memorial Hospital, sometime in August, Phil had begun to wheeze and his eyes had turned a cold, dark, gray, Southerland writes in his book:

> *Baby Phil weighed 14 pounds, down from 24 a week earlier. They actually put him on a glucose IV, the absolute worst thing they could do. He grew limp and still, and, panicked, she ran into the hall calling for help "Is he going to die? Can*

somebody tell me, is he going to die?" No one could tell her what was happening. Joanna refers to it as the "ketone death rattle," an unimaginable wheeze that she describes as sounding like a knock on death's door. "He was going fast," she said. "I could feel it … he was dying."

While Joanna prayed, her husband was sitting in a chair squeezing the arms until his knuckles were white. Phil was being attended to frantically. "Two hours passed quickly," Joanna says and the doctor came in and spoke. "I've got good news and bad news. The good news is he's going to live." Joanna started weeping with joy before the bad news could be revealed. Her son would live and that was everything. Anything after that could be dealt with. The doctor continued … "but he has diabetes. The youngest case of juvenile diabetes we've ever seen."

DETERMINATION RUNS IN THE FAMILY

Phil's determination to dominate diabetes plays out daily in his life. His attitude is not surprising at all, given that his devoted mother not only saved his life that day by bringing him to the emergency room, but was also determined that, despite all the grim news and predictions, her son lead as healthy and fruitful a life as possible.

In *Not Dead Yet*, Phil writes about Joanna's response:

"Dead by 25, eh?" Joanna said in response to the doctor telling him that Phil's life would be dramatically shortened as a result of this diagnosis. *Not if I have anything to say about it!* "You don't," was the response, "there's not much you can do." *Oh yes there is. There are days and months and years of things I can do. There are books to be read, opinions to be gathered, lists to be made, friends and neighbors to be mobilized. There are things we can do.*

That attitude and commitment cements for me what it truly takes to mobilize around fear and uncertainty. Focus on your goals, not your fears. It's a life lesson for all of us. By putting the focus on what you can control and what you can affect, you waste less energy and resources in worrying about the end results. Focusing only on what you can do systematically will help you reach your desired outcome. For Joanna, that outcome was about giving Phil a life that he could enjoy living for a long time.

IT TAKES A VILLAGE

Joanna Southerland is a dedicated, loving and committed individual who did all that was in her power to give her child a healthy outlook on life and an opportunity to thrive with a chronic disease. Nothing got in the way of her single-minded focus to improve the life of her son. As a result, the world has benefited greatly.

Joanna is a complete joy to speak with. Quick-witted and full of stories, she recalls long-ago moments with the vividness of yesterday. She explains to me that her complete focus from Phil's diagnosis day was on immersing herself in literature, books, medical journals, nutritionists and support groups.

Her husband at the time, a former competitive marathoner, was a lawyer, and Joanna was able to discontinue working as a marketing director for a German steel company to turn her energy and commitment to her baby boy.

Unfortunately, this would not last very long. Joanna's husband began drinking heavily and the stress was running high for her. On the next doctor's visit, a resident at the University of South Florida looked at Joanna and saw a very tired and depleted woman. "Your son is doing fine, he said, "but you're going to have a breakdown." She explained the situation at home, how she was pouring all of her energy into learning as much as she could while also trying to manage an alcoholic husband. This doctor, who Joanna thanks to this very day, looked at her and said, "You can't survive a drunk and a boy with diabetes. You need to do what you have to do."

With that, Joanna became a single mother.

As a single mother battling diabetes in the early '80s with little technology and understanding of the disease, Joanna felt alone and scared. Recognizing that she could not take care of Phil alone, Joanna rallied neighbors, friends, teachers, local business owners and a community of people who would serve as her small army.

It truly takes a village. One person from that village that Phil has especially fond memories of is Kevin Davis, a family friend who became a surrogate dad for him. Kevin was a successful real estate agent and became very active in Phil's life, coaching his baseball team and playing racquetball with him on weekends, as well as providing emotional and mental support. When Phil got older, Kevin would drive him around for talks and Phil would even babysit Kevin's kids.

I've talked with other single parents and life is difficult enough without a chronic disease. Why should single parents feel like they can't reach out for help? What I've learned from Joanna is that it's critical. The worry or anxiety over someone not managing diabetes as well as they can does not overcome this simple fact. We simply can't manage or overcome diabetes on our own. We need support. Joanna recognized this early on and rallied her village to educate and help them understand what signs to look for in Phil and what to do in an emergency. "Everyone knew that I knew what I was doing," Phil says, "but if there was an emergency or if I was flopping on the ground, people had a toolkit and knew what to do. Joanna was way ahead of her time on that, both in finding a support network, but more importantly, understanding the need to educate others about my condition." As with anything in life, when demands get too high and challenges present themselves, our best and most efficient way to slow things down is to spread that out to ready, willing, trusted and able people.

~~~~~~

A Personal View: Our Village

I know without a doubt that I would not be able to do this without my wife. Together, we share this burden and together we experience all the literal (and figurative) highs and lows. We learn from each other, we help each other. For example, every night we alternate the bedtime blood sugar check and who gets up with Gavin the following morning. The extra sleep and knowledge that we can let go for short periods of time allow us to renew, recharge and be at our best for all the demands in our lives, not the least of which is managing and overcoming type 1 diabetes on a daily basis.

In addition to bearing the heavier load of managing Gavin, Tara orders and handles all the supplies and I make sure the numbers are uploaded consistently to help us tweak and calculate necessary corrections and insulin dosing. Even with that, we both realize that the heaviest burden is Gavin's in being the subject of so many calculations, discussions, prickings and prod-dings. His day—like that of so many others—starts and ends the same way: with a finger prick and, perhaps, an insulin shot.

We are also fortunate in having amazing caretakers who have become not only a part of our family, but have served as our surrogates for Gavin's care so Tara, in addition to her own job as an interior designer, does not have to play nurse or on-call doctor all day.

Tara's decision to find support on a dedicated website for chronic illness caretakers was key to our accessing caretakers who had type 1 diabetes that we could learn from as well. Whether it's www.childrenwith diabetes.com or www.care.com, which is more broad, there are resources out there to help and support you.

One treasured helper we have is Faye NeSmith, who is known respectfully and deservedly as Miss Faye, a home-based teacher fashioned in the traditional model of preschool care. Every week, Miss Faye gathers five to eight preschoolers in one of their homes and delights them with crafts and games and facilitates learning in ways that you can only hope they get in the structured school system. Her commitment to children and to our family, especially in learning all about type 1 diabetes to care for Gavin, have made a remarkable difference in helping us spread out his care.

Savannah Day, at only 25, has been a part of our family for almost five years since we first moved to Atlanta. From the day I opened the door for our first babysitter appointment, her smile and youthful attitude continue to make us smile. Born deaf and told she'd likely never hear in her life, Savannah struggled with her speech and her education. After receiving a cochlear implant at age 8 she was diagnosed with type 1 diabetes at 11. This is a girl who draws upon an inner strength to keep forging ahead, finding ways to improve and give back at the same time. Savannah is working on her physical therapy assistant degree while holding two jobs and battling type 1. There's always another perspective, and if you can gain empathy for what some people have to go through, it has a way of inspiring you to dig even deeper, whether for yourself or someone you love with type 1 diabetes. What Savannah has taught me is that no matter how hard you think you have it, there's always someone who has it harder.

Another babysitter, Rachel Halverson, is at first shy. But she is confident and fiercely independent, qualities that help us feel assured when we leave our children in her care. A semi-professional cellist who has been practicing from the age of 11, Rachel has a work ethic and an independence that I don't really see from her generation Y compatriots. Music changed her life upon reaching high school with the first piece she ever played with a symphony, "The Moldau" by Bedrich Smetana. Rachel credits music for helping her overcome her shyness, developing leadership skills, life-long relationships, and a better understanding of human emotions. She is another great example of how important a sense of overall purpose is in leading a life while having to manage diabetes. She's had to earn her success and place in music, and as with any type 1, has had the additional obstacles that have shaped and cultivated a diligent, responsible and courageous young woman.

Nurse Jean and teachers at St. Benedict's Episcopal School are our caretakers from 8:00 a.m. to 12:30 p.m. every weekday. Gavin was their first student with type 1 diabetes. They don't treat Gavin any differently, and have been more than willing to really understand diabetes and manage it so Gavin can focus on his education and be there in the same way as all the other kids. Nurse Jean is from Trinidad, and her Caribbean lilt makes you immediately feel more relaxed. She has a genuine ability to stay calm and level, which is wonderful for Gavin. While at first it made Tara a bit uncomfortable because she felt that sometimes Jean wasn't taking the diabetes seriously enough, she has learned that it's just Jean's style and she cares deeply and lovingly for Gavin.

Our love and appreciation for Faye NeSmith, Savannah Day, Rachel Halverson, Nurse Jean and St. Benedict's runs deep. Their care and affection for Gavin have helped free our lives from being dominated by constant care and monitoring.

It may not sound so dramatic, but their presence and contribution make a dramatic difference in avoiding our own burnout and personal sustainability. It also gives our precious boy everything he needs because he's the one impacted. We don't stop there, however. As Joanna recognized, mobilizing, recruiting and finding support groups are a wonderful way to meet like-minded people with the same thoughts, questions and concerns. It's also a great way to constantly refine how you approach managing type 1 by learning best practices.

~~~~~~

At one support group, Joanna met a new woman to the group who was accompanied by her mother. She was a 35-year-old type 1 woman, frail looking and timid, with a nervous and uncertain demeanor. A switch went on for Joanna in how she would have to manage her son's disease after she saw how delicately and passively this woman's mother interacted with her. Joanna knew she would have to be tough and set clear and specific boundaries for Phil.

A DIFFERENT NORMAL

Because Phil was diagnosed so young, he feels that his life with diabetes has been easier for him than perhaps those who were diagnosed later in life. After all, his "normal" is diabetes. Phil does not experience the burnout that he hears so often of others. "People who are thought leaders in the diabetes community talk about vacations from checking themselves," he says. "I couldn't imagine that because I want to be in control. That has always been there for me." He realized that, in a way, being diagnosed at age 7 months was a blessing when he saw other kids at a diabetes camp who had recently been diagnosed and were bitter and confused about it. "They went to this camp, in part to feel normal—to feel like they weren't outcasts because of a disease that had suddenly, and without any fault of their own, irrevocably changed their lives," he writes in his book. That makes such a huge difference because while they may not harbor guilt about the disease, having done nothing to get it, they do feel different and alone and that can lead to anger and rebellion.

Like my son who was diagnosed at 22 months, it's just a different normal. With that, it doesn't change the fact that it's hard and, no doubt, there will be rebellion and push-back.

For Phil, that push-back was brief. When he was about 4 years old, before his parents' divorce at age 6, he would run out of the house and hide behind his neighbor's house to avoid getting insulin shots. He describes his father as being unmoved by this. His father would drag him home and give him the belt, the classic old-style Southern method of child-rearing. After that, Phil says he took to giving himself injections without much resistance. Phil gives his father credit, saying that it was "one of the only contributions to the management of my disease at that point in my life, but a very significant one," Phil writes.

Phil also credits his father with having Phil inject him with saline to show him that (a) taking a shot is not that bad and (b) it must be done. It was Joanna who somehow communicated at that early age that if he took the shots he would be OK and that if he didn't, he would not. Phil became excited to take control of his body, and as he's demonstrated with most of his bike races, he has not looked back. At the age of 6, Phil became the "CEO of his body," as he tells me. "It was also simpler back then," he says. "You didn't have to adjust for everything, I basically had to take three shots a day." He adds: "Controlling diabetes is hard, but once you figure it out, everything in your life becomes easier. Everything just gets better."

MOVING AWAY FROM PAIN

Among the many things I'm learning in the early stages of parenting a young person with diabetes is that while love is paramount to a child's well-being, tough love in dealing with this disease is sometimes crucial and necessary. Not every parent is comfortable with the concept of "tough love," however. If you're not, find someone with that ability in your child's or loved one's sphere of influence and utilize that person. It's like any good coach. If you want people to fully realize their potential and break out of comfort zones, sometimes that requires pain.

We need to remember that one of the very basic survival premises of human beings is to move toward pleasure and away from pain. "Whatever works," Phil tells me. "I'm more of a fan of the 'Here's what you can do if you take control' and 'Here's why you want to take control.'" That said, he adds, "There are some people who refuse to open their eyes to that and they end up with A1Cs at 10 or higher, essentially killing themselves. They need to know there is a consequence to their actions, both good and bad." An A1C is the common term for the result of the HbA1c test, done every three months to give an indication of average blood glucose levels during that period. A higher number indicates higher general levels of blood glucose during those three months.

Phil explains this very simply for a parent in that it's no different than telling your child the benefits of getting good grades—get into a good college, find a job you love, be independent—as well as the consequences of getting bad grades—don't get into a good school and work for lower wages in a job you don't love. Reward systems and encouragement, while vital, simply don't get you all the way home in every case. Avoiding pain is often a far greater motivator for sustained behavioral change. Joanna understood this profoundly, but used it highly selectively.

Highlighted in Phil's book is a clear example. One day when Phil was about 6 years old, he asked his mother for cake at a birthday party. She said it would be OK, but that he had to do his shot first.

"I don't wanna do my shot. I just want the cake."

"Fine, you'll go blind."

"Huh?"

"Don't do your shot, don't take care of yourself, you'll be blind by age 22."

Simple, straightforward "avoid pain" motivation. That is tough love in its purest form.

Phil says that got his attention. "While to a 6-year-old the age of 22 seems like a far-off distant time, I was still old enough to be scared by the idea of blindness." Who wouldn't?!

With this style of parenting, Phil learned to accept his diabetes at a very young age. He understood that diabetes had to be put in its place. Phil accepted what he had to do and got on with his life. "I just don't really have an alternative. Instead of being dominated by the disease, I'd learned to make it work for me, or at least not get in the way of doing what I wanted," he wrote in his book. As a young and competitive athlete, Phil realized early on that for him to be good, his blood sugar had to be good. "If I wanted to have a chance at competing then I had to take control," he told me in an interview. Phil figured that out very early on when he took up swimming at the age of 5. "If my blood sugar was good, I swam well. If it wasn't, then I failed," he told me. "Lots of other young people with type 1 do this, I've learned," he writes. "Taking this view usually requires a little help and support from others—in my case, the number one supporter was and still is my Mom."

As a parent to a son, I am inspired and moved by this relationship. A mother's love for her son can likely only be truly understood by mothers and the commitment that Joanna made early in Phil's life has produced an amazing individual with a narrow focus, coupled with a big picture mission.

UNRELENTING DETERMINATION

When I first met Phil, I felt like I knew him for a long time. Open and friendly, Phil's demeanor is gentle and genuine, but you can clearly see the grit and toughness that have been embedded in his character. As he casually munches on some morning fiber in the form of a bran muffin, he speaks matter of factly about what he's doing in the world. That's the quality that I have come to love about Phil and his type 1 friends who he's been so open to introduce me to. Humility: a humble confidence with a fierce ambition.

One story described in his book that amazes me about Phil is this quality packed with raw determination. One night before a big race, Phil had a seizure. When asked how his team's competition reacted when they found out, his answer was that they didn't tell anyone. He didn't go around advertising the fact he had diabetes. His attitude was, "I'm here to race bikes, so let's race." Phil never let diabetes be an excuse, although he easily could have. What others considered a disadvantage, he thought of as just an obstacle to overcome. He has risen above it. What I have come to learn about Phil and his management of type 1 is that he applies the same unrelenting determination to everything he does including making sure his blood sugar is optimized so that everything in his life can be optimized. For him to be good, it starts with his blood sugar being good. He's right: Who cares if someone has diabetes? Let's get on with what we're here to do.

Phil Southerland and Team Novo Nordisk are a force in the world, helping people every single day living with this condition. It was back in 2005 that Phil combined his passion for racing and his mission of raising awareness to form the team of athletes, some of whom had diabetes. Their mission remains the same through today:

We strive to instill hope and inspiration for people around the world affected by diabetes. With appropriate diet, exercise, treatment and technology, we believe anyone with diabetes can achieve their dreams. (www.teamnovonordisk.com)

Whether it's meeting with youth who are off-track with their diabetes management to providing test strips to underprivileged children throughout Africa, Phil and Team Novo Nordisk use their inner strength and determination, all that have made them successful in sport and in life to better the lives of others. By combining racing, sports research, philanthropy and global outreach, Team Novo Nordisk has gone from a grassroots organization to one of the most prodigious global organizations to inspire the worldwide diabetes community to properly manage diabetes, gain broader access to insulin, and live a better life.

For Joanna, a prouder mom is hard to find. Phil's accomplishments notwithstanding, Joanna is most proud of raising a resilient, courageous and kind individual. The rest for her is just a dream. She first realized that Phil was spreading his wings when she called him during the first few weeks of college checking up on him and his diabetes. "Mom, you're driving me crazy. I know what I need to do," he said.

LEARNING TO LET GO

One of the hardest things for Joanna was letting go of her son. It's hard enough by itself, even harder based on the fact that your child has to carry the burden of this disease. "This is a serious disease," Joanna says, "but I had to let him go, it was necessary to let him go. My life was diabetes all those years, it still is, but it's Phil's life."

The letting go, while the hardest part, turns out to be the fuel for achievement and the gift of growth. Phil's force in the world could not have truly happened without this letting go from the most trusted and loving supporter he would ever know. He just knew he needed to and with his wings spread far and wide, he soars to new heights with a drive, ambition and spirit that continue to impact millions of lives around him.

DIALED IN

Our time together in this latest meeting is drawing to a close and Phil checks his continuous glucose monitor, a tiny sensor placed under the skin to check glucose levels in tissue fluid. "I was 105 when we started talking and I'm 107 now," he says observationally. Phil is supremely warm and confident. His assuredness around his condition is inspiring and impressive. I ask him if he can get better around managing his blood sugar. "We all can get better," he says with a smile, "but I'm pretty dialed in."

Dialed in is a great way to characterize Phil. He knows who he is and what he stands for. He's not only changing lives, he's changing diabetes, literally. Phil and Team Novo Nordisk are committed to learning, translating and educating the world on diabetes management. "I'm most excited about introducing our new look to the world," he says. Together they are embarking on an unprecedented and ambitious plan to collect data on their athletes, translate that data, and then work with health care organizations and people with diabetes around the world to empower and educate. Phil adds, "We will have the largest database of diabetes information in the world. If you're a recently diagnosed kid in Australia, then there will be someone who knows the Team Novo Nordisk protocol in that region. The world is my market." The team now has a medical staff of eight people and growing, comprised of nutrition-ists, medical doctors and others dedicated to the science of diabetes management. "We want to better educate people with diabetes for what's truly possible as well as everyday people, and provide access to insulin," Phil says. "There are tools and technology to really take control of your condition. What motivates me today is not the chance of winning a bike race, but of changing behaviors on a global scale, " he adds. On the 100th anniversary of the discovery of insulin in 2021, you can be sure that Team Novo Nordisk will be celebrating. With a clear purpose and passion to grow the team with 100% type 1 athletes across a variety of sports, it is still Phil's sport that will represent the ultimate dream of the organization he has created—competing in the Tour de France.

Changing diabetes isn't just a slogan and Phil knows there's work to be done. Much of the world does not have access to in-sulin or the education required to understand how to view the condition. "In many parts of the world, diabetes is the cause of so many 'You can'ts'," he says. "When your son Gavin goes to school, we want other kids to look at him and say, 'You know, diabetes is cool, there are professional teams of type 1 athletes, maybe he'll be part of that team one day.' We want diabetes to now be the cause of 'You can.'"

Phil is changing the typecast on type 1 diabetes, and is com-municating a message of overcoming obstacles and not using your condition as an excuse by example and determined leadership. When a kid is diagnosed with type 1, the first thing Phil will say to him is, "Welcome to the team." They can walk proudly now because they are automatically a part of his team. He follows that up with "What's your dream?" Phil knows how to immediately connect diabetes management to what is important to a child or even an adult. "Everyone has dreams," he says excitedly. "I try to find out what their aspirations are and help them understand that by hitting A1C goals they can stand on our shoulders and reach their dreams."

The year 2021 represents a not-too-distant future that Phil sees more clearly than others. He sees a world of sustainable access to insulin and to give those with type 1 diabetes the empowerment they need by putting an all type 1 team in cycling's biggest and most competitive race, the Tour de France. Phil leaves me by saying, "We're not going to put a rider in the Tour de France, we're going to put a *team* of type 1 riders into the Tour de France." That lofty goal represents the ambition and a simple, but powerful message for everyone—you can do anything with diabetes.

TOM KARLYA

Actor, Diabetes Advocate
Two children diagnosed—Kaitlin in 1992 at age 2
and Rob in 2009 at age 13

OF ALL THE ROLES THAT ACTOR TOM KARLYA HAS PLAYED, IT IS his role as "Diabetes Dad" that will end up earning him lifetime achievement, in my opinion. As with most lifetime achievement earners, it was never Tom's intent to be recognized in this way. He could not have anticipated that his one clear goal—finding a cure for type 1 diabetes for his children and the millions suffering from this disease—would define his adult life.

There was a time when Tom was single-mindedly focused on another cause: his acting career. He was one of the few who crossed over from television to live stage performances and film, and doors were beginning to open. A regular in the theatrical smash hit *Tony n' Tina's Wedding* with the original New York cast, Tom's success was growing in front of the camera as well, with appearances in shows such as *NYPD Blue*, *Law & Order*, *The Cosby Show*, *Spin City*, commercials and even a few movies.

Actors will tell you they prepare for surprises on the set. But on Sept. 26, 1992, with his career flying high, Tom got news that put in motion a role he never saw coming. It required the performance of his life.

Tom's daughter, Kaitlyn, was 2 years old and his wife, Jill, had taken her to the pediatrician because her diapers were constantly soaked and she wasn't well. The doctor checked Kaitlyn's blood sugar and gave Jill the news: Get her to the hospital. Frantic, she called Tom from the doctor's office.

"Tom, I'm taking Kaitlyn directly to the emergency room. Tom … they think it's diabetes," Jill told him.

Two hours later, Tom sat down next to his little girl in the hospital and said, "Hi, honey." Kaitlyn was gray in color and she was all cried out. She had been pricked and poked what seemed like a million times and she was exhausted. He pushed her hair away from her eyes as she looked around the room and noticed all the wires and machines she was hooked up to.

"Daddy?"

"What is it, honey?"

"Fix."

Right then and there, Tom made a commitment that he would not quit until diabetes is cured. That commitment has only become stronger over the years.

"At Kaitlyn's crib in the hospital upon diagnosis, I made up my mind then that I would not bow to this disease and I would not let anyone I come in contact with her bow to it, either," Tom said. "If we do that, diabetes wins and surely I will not let diabetes win. I had to deal with learning and I had to deal with moving forward. I said from the beginning that I must always be learning and always be willing to hear what others have to say. No one has made more mistakes than me, so as one who educates and lectures, I start often by saying that point. I suck at this every day. But don't we all? It is the moving forward that is so crucial."

THE ELEPHANT IN THE ROOM

This would only be the beginning of the central role that diabetes would play in the Karlya household. Enter the elephant in the room for any multi-child family where one has been diagnosed with diabetes: the possibility of a second diagnosis. When our younger son was diagnosed, I know that it didn't take Tara very long to start ruminating on if or when our older son might get the disease as well. At this early stage not knowing much or anything about diabetes can lead you to places in your mind that can cause great fear and uncertainty. It was the same for the Karlyas: total disbelief and uncertainty. One of Tara's first questions when we met with endocrinologists was a very candid, "So what are the chances my other son will get it?" It turns out that siblings have about a 1% greater risk of getting diabetes than the average person. One percent never seemed like a big number to us and from what we have seen and learned it seems that it should be higher than that. Perhaps it is because multi-diagnosed families tend to be more active in type 1 causes, so you hear more of their stories.

A Personal View: Fight or Flight

Upon hearing Tom's story, I remembered what it was like to get the news of our son's diagnosis. Before you can even try to assimilate what is going on as you deal with an emotional override of the brain, you're forced to hold back your emotions and bring your logical, rational "thinking" mind back into the forefront. What many of us have experienced during this grim transfer of news is what is known as "fight or flight," the biological phenomenon linked to our own survival. You know you're in fight or flight mode when you feel the rush of stress hormones and you lose a sense of time and place as your blood flows to your extremities at the same time your thinking mind begins to shut down. In the midst of that, the doctor asks you to think and act *now*. It was a jarring experience, and for Tom and Jill and all the parents whose children's welfare far outweighs their own, it leaves its branded and lasting psychological impact.

For the Karlyas, the 1% odds turned out to be high enough. In 2009, their son, Rob, was diagnosed as well. What materialized in the Karlya home is what many parents fear on a regular basis. It's the dark shadow looming that adds to the emotional toll the disease takes on caretakers. Will it happen? When will it happen? How will it happen? Will we catch it in time? He seems to be peeing more often. Should we enroll him in a TrialNet study? Do we find out if she has antibodies or just live our lives and hope for the best?

A Personal View

These thoughts of uncertainty and fear exact a toll that's hard to quantify, but are very real. Dr. Avril Beckford shares, "To the extent that couples discuss, share and communicate their feelings around this uncertainty can go a long way to calming this concern and therefore, bolstering the marriage and the family."

When the Karlyas came up against these fears, it was after Rob made a comment you hear quite a bit before a diagnosis.

"Hey Dad, I've been peeing a lot," Rob said matter-of-factly.

"What's a lot?" asked Tom.

"Four times an hour."

Tom went into diagnosing mode. "Since when?"

"Um, since yesterday," Rob answered. And, finally, as only a sibling of a child who has diabetes would say, "That's diabetes, isn't it?"

Tom told his son to have Kaitlyn, who was 19, check his blood sugar.

"She came downstairs with the meter hanging limply in her hand at her side. She was white as a sheet," Tom said. " 'Dad, the meter just says high.' We knew that meant that his blood sugar, normally ranging from 80 to 120, was up over 600. We took him to the emergency room to confirm what we already knew. Our second child was diagnosed with type 1 diabetes."

~~~~~~

A Personal View

I have found that using one child's meter and strips to check the other child to rule out diabetes is a fairly common act, although it's not a way of diagnosing diabetes. It confirms that most of us either expect the worst or just want to quickly rule out the worst. As a result, parents and siblings of children who have diabetes are very sensitive to the slightest change in a non-diagnosed child's behavior or symptoms. And, why wouldn't we be? Let's face it, this is a tough condition to live with and despite learning how to deal with it and perhaps life getting even easier with it over time, the last thing we need is to go through it again, no matter how well equipped we are. I mean, isn't one child enough? Do we really have to relive all of this and watch yet another child go through it? I remember when my close friend, Steve Gabbay, whose daughter was diagnosed at 20 months, said to me. "You'll deal with it and it gets easier over time, but it sucks." How true is that?

DIABETES DOUBLED

So, just like that, the dark shadow fell and diabetes hit the Karlyas for a second time. Tom always thought they were in for more, and admits he had no real basis for that feeling; we all can relate. Tom's main thought at the time: "This has to be a real cruel joke."

It certainly does seem unfair that this would happen twice or more in the same family. Tara and I both have our times when we feel thankful that Jake does not have type 1 diabetes, while we occasionally worry that he will get it. I certainly don't worry obsessively as there is nothing I can do about it. The story I tell myself is that if he were to get diabetes, we would be that much more equipped to handle it. We already know how to do it. Tom is perfectly candid when he speaks of how Rob getting diagnosed at age 13 was both harder and easier.

"It's just emotionally taxing," Tom says. "It's everything times two." There are double reminders everywhere: daily management times two, a full closet of diabetes supplies instead of a half, two school nurses, two 504 plans and the list goes on.

Of course, the timing of this event happening can also shape how much harder or easier managing diabetes in the home can be. The Karlyas had to re-learn managing diabetes in the adolescent years, since Rob was diagnosed at 13. "Kaitlyn was 2," Tom says. "She never knew any differently."

A Personal View

It is the same for us with Gavin. He was 22 months old when he was diagnosed. He never will know any differently. This is one of the most prevalent statements I hear from doctors, friends and others who have been connected to type 1 diabetes. I think it is powerful to interpret the story that way. If a child doesn't know any differently, that must make it easier, right? Well, that's not the whole story. I do believe that in many ways it does make it easier and I certainly remind myself of that when my heart aches after failed blood sugar checks, difficult lows, irritability from highs or times when this disease is at its ugliest. An early diagnosis in life means that a child will never know what it is like to not have diabetes. That's the good news. The bad news: It also means that a child may never know what it is like to *not* have diabetes.

Sometimes I feel this is the part that many people do not understand. As I've learned in my sales experience, every benefit has a cost. Part of this benefit of not knowing any differently comes at a cost of not knowing what it must be like to have a day free of vigilance and background worry. While I agree that Kaitlyn's, Gavin's and others' early diagnosis means they don't have to compare it to another life they were leading, it doesn't change the fact that it means that more of their childhood is spent dealing with the disease. As Tom puts it, "It's not, 'Why us?' but rather, 'Why would another childhood be stolen?'" Here's where dealing with both aspects of this story for a healthy outlook can be very empowering. Not knowing any differently in some ways makes things easier by not having to compare your pre-diabetes experience, but it is also important to not assume that somehow it makes it easier for a child diagnosed earlier in life.

On the easier side of a second child getting diagnosed, you are likely to have support from your sibling. "The transition for Rob was stark," Tom says. "But, it was somehow made easier that Kaitlyn already had it." Their family was already acclimated and had its own imprint on managing diabetes in their home. Rob's diagnosis just made the imprint deeper. "The more active you are in managing the disease, the more knowledgeable you are. The more knowledgeable you are, the better position you are in to provide care, effect change and support one another."

PASSION AND PURPOSE

It's interesting how rich and meaningful people's lives are who work in this arena. It is more powerful than anything I have ever seen in the corporate arena and it confirms for me that we all need deep purpose and passion to fuel our lives—to stand for something, to move from the mindset of asking what keeps you up at night to what gets you out of bed in the morning. This is another area that Tom has reached that very few people ever get to, and something that acting alone, may not have given him—passion and purpose, a meaningful life.

When I ask Tom about the impact of Kaitlyn's diagnosis, he recalls a story that illustrated for me what kind of commitment, passion and fire Tom has for finding a cure. One day several years after her diagnosis, Kaitlyn said to him, "Dad, your eyes light up when you talk about movies. I took that from you the day I was diagnosed." Tom knew this was an incredible burden for a young girl to bear. He looked her in the eyes and did what any great actor would do—connect with honest emotion and authenticity—except this wasn't acting. He reminded her about his relationships and true friends who were there for him and promised to do their part to rally for a cure.

There is Phil Rosenthal, who Tom was friendly with before the producer went on to commercial success and notoriety for *Everybody Loves Raymond*. The friendship produced one of the most inspiring and uplifting experiences of his life when he was able to shoot public service announcements with Ray Romano.

There is his tenure on *dLife*, the wonderful diabetes program on CNBC featuring stories, recipes and diabetes education, for which he was nominated for an Emmy award. That led to his friend and former agent, Doug Kestin, calling Tom to let him know he was perfect for a part years after Tom gave up acting for advocating. It reminded him that he reached a level of success in acting that very few people in the profession will ever attain.

With that, he looked deep into his daughter's eyes and smiled.

"So, tell me again what you took from me, honey?"

It was settled. She never asked again about what she thought he gave up for her. She understood that Tom was now leading a life with greater purpose and meaning than he had ever known.

A MAN WITH A MISSION

One of Tom's greatest diabetes accomplishments is the millions of dollars he has helped raise for the Diabetes Research Institute at the University of Miami School of Medicine. Tom is vice president of the institute's foundation.

The Diabetes Research Institute

If the DRI was a secret institute, I'd compare it to the movie *Men in Black*. This, however, should be no secret. Within this building are some of the world's most capable people in a dedicated and tireless pursuit of one thing: finding a cure for diabetes.

The understated building was a gift from the Building Construction Trades Department of the AFL-CIO, the largest organizing union for construction workers in the U.S. and Canada. The BCTD, through bucket collections, walkathons, motorcycle rallies, golf tournaments and more, raised $45 million to build the DRI and didn't stop there. After the building was completed in 1994, 100% union, BCTD wanted to help fund the research as well. It is important to recognize this gift and what it set in motion because the DRI is most ambitious about one track of diabetes: find a cure. While we all want to manage this disease better, and thankfully, wonderful technology allows us to do that, it is the DRI that works tirelessly to eradicate it. The DRI in Miami has partners worldwide toward that end—it's the hub of the DRI Federation, a global network of leading diabetes research centers in 20 countries that pulls the best researchers and scientists on the planet.

The DRI is like any other medical building you've been to. Since the building is relatively old, there is nothing that speaks to the lofty mission of what they are doing when you walk into the lobby—until you get to the directory. As I scan the directory for Gary Kleiman, senior director of medical development, I can't help but notice that there is not one word on the six floors at the DRI that I truly understand. Each floor has its own path to a cure or supporting paths: immunology, islet cell physiology, molecular biology, tissue engineering, immunogenetics and islet cell transplant.

What I quickly learn is that what is going on inside these old walls is the newest in technology, human capital and scientific insight that the diabetes world has to offer. Inside are the hearts and minds of people working daily on our behalf to end diabetes. That is not a light mission and it casts a sense of urgency on its people that doesn't intimidate, but fuels them. They know they are recognized as working at the most advanced research center of its kind. This amazing team is hard at work, relentlessly driving for a cure, and equally open and humble. After one phone call, Gary is gracious enough to meet with me and introduce me to one of his colleagues, Chris Fraker.

When I meet Gary, I am immediately drawn to his smile, humble appearance and sense of gratitude to still be with us. Gary was diagnosed with type 1 diabetes at 6 years old in 1960. I also notice that one eye has failed and as I learn about his past health issues, I realize the toll this disease can take. Gary has been at this work since the early 1970s. His parents were among the initial handful of families that founded the DRI and Gary has witnessed the amazing progress and setbacks that have occurred in this building for four decades. We talk about the latest breakthroughs, new hopes and old scientific discoveries that creep back to the current conversations about figuring out a biological cure. I can feel his enthusiasm and passion only tempered with so many "almost" moments. You see, Gary is on his second donor kidney, he has received an islet transplant that made him insulin-free for two years until either the new islet cells slowly failed (he still has some working) or were attacked by his immune system yet again. Early on, doctors told him that he would not see a cure or a meaningful breakthrough in his generation so he now knows not to believe anyone who wants to limit your thinking or curb your dreams. He's seen amazing discoveries and has pioneered as a participant in biological breakthroughs. You can tell Gary is still a dreamer, but with his years dealing with a disease he is trying to cure, he has an air of pragmatism as well. He has limited sight in his "good" eye, is unable to drive, has had multiple surgeries on tendons in his hands, elbows and feet from years of anti-rejection drugs and complications from type 1, and yet he carries on despite the pain, hardship and difficulty of his mission—deeply knowing that despite the great challenge of living his life with type 1 diabetes, he has a real shot at curing it.

I've rarely met someone so excited to be doing what he's doing, particularly when you consider the chronic challenges he has had to endure. As he walks me around the halls to meet other people, he gets hugs and big smiles and he's quick with a joke. He takes me to the second floor where amazing work is being done to use bioengineering techniques to protect transplanted islets as well as provide these insulin-producing cells with the critical nutrients found in the native environment.

When Gary introduces me to Chris, Chris is busy working with both hands while we begin talking. As he finishes what he was doing, he quickly washes up, shakes my hand, and engages with me as if he's working on a project. He has thick, brown hair, a relaxed demeanor, and, despite working in a lab, he's in shorts and a short sleeve button down. His attention and soft intensity make me feel extremely important. I am a parent of a type 1 child and it occurs to me that this is meaningful for Chris. Additionally, I am sure that this is how Chris is with everyone. As he shares his background in education and science, it's fairly obvious to me that this guy could be working anywhere. Chris is also type 1 and has a high-risk daughter. He comes to work every day with the passion to cure this disease and the brain to have a chance at it. Chris is a bit of a jack-of-all trades engineer, which is quite amazing given how complex and intricate one path of research might be. As he begins to describe some areas of his work, I realize that I don't understand any of it—improving cell encapsulation by understanding reasons of failure and "turning on" protective mechanisms within actual cells by providing local oxygen and immune modulation. He's also working with the stem cell group, which is looking at the role of oxygen and other local, environmental factors in influencing the differentiation of stem cells into insulin-producing cells. While I don't understand it completely, I do understand that Chris and the researchers at DRI are not only equipped to bring us a future without finger pricks and constant insulin dependency, they are up to the task as well.

Chris, like others at DRI, challenges convention. When you're trying to cure a disease, you have to be open to new ways of doing things. "I am always looking for something," Chris says wryly. "I'm a healthy skeptic." For Chris, he's challenged mentally, trying to solve a puzzle every day. Connecting those pieces is personal as well. Chris shares with me that he may very well have been doing this work even if he was not type 1 because of its complexity and how far we've come in advancing to a point where a real cure is in sight. While doctors may have said that a cure would not be in Gary's generation, I am electrified when I feel Chris' intense belief that it will happen in his. Chris shows me the lab where they remove islet cells from the pancreas, speaks of the challenge in sourcing healthy islet cells and even shares a few helpful tips on continuous glucose monitor use, which we're considering. This guy knows his business and all I want to do is spend more time learning and understanding what he does. But I also have a sense of urgency to get Chris back to the important work he's doing. I come away with a wonderful feeling and I can't quite grasp it. Of course, there was the fact that there are these amazing people dedicated to a cure for Gavin and millions of others, but it's more than that. I realize what it is when I'm in the cab heading to the airport and a smile overtakes me. Chris asked me to come back with Gavin, but in the meantime, to send him a message. "Tell him he's not alone." I remember that and I start to cry. That's it. The feeling that Gavin and millions of others who suffer from this disease are not alone. They need to know it. I cannot wait to take Gavin back there.

It's important for me to mention that Gary and Chris are two of the many people at DRI with type 1 diabetes or who have a relative with it. "It's one of the intangibles that give DRI its heartbeat," Gary says. I am humbled and grateful that there is such a place operating at a very high level with a clear focus that is truly at the heart of what we all want: ending diabetes, its management and the long-term complications that can result.

Tom has made the DRI and what it does his mission. "Tom does so much for us," says Gary Kleiman, senior director of medical development, "not the least of which he is 'feet on the street.'" I completely get it. With Tom's personality, commitment and zeal around finding a cure for his children, it makes complete sense that he would also dedicate his efforts to enabling the one place that he felt that was closest to his dream—a cure for Kaitlyn and Rob. Tom is an ambassador utilizing all of his skills and knowledge in an organization that shares his clearly defined philosophy.

Tom serves as a key liaison for the DRI Diabetes Diplomats program that has been instrumental in raising funds all over the country. Diabetes Diplomats are people from all ages all over the world creating fun, simple and creative ways to raise money and to be a part of the cure. Tom fuels this campaign by working with individuals who share his dedication and commit to flowing dollars to make a cure a reality.

Tom also works closely with the union that has been integral to the DRI's growth. The Building Construction Trades Department of the AFL-CIO came on board in 1984 with their Blueprint for Cure, a separate fundraising effort to fund and build a dedicated state of the art facility focused on finding a cure. This was part of the plan laid out by the founding scientific director, Dr. Daniel H. Mintz, and families committed to making sure the future was different than the past. Dollars Against Diabetes or D.A.D. is an annual campaign organized by BCTD and the signature effort for Blueprint for Cure. With the help of state and local councils around the country, the D.A.D.'s Day campaign has been able to donate more than $40 million to the Diabetes Research Institute. Tom finds himself at the center of this effort, assisting or managing 75 different events around the country, including the Labor of Love golf tournament.

The corporate sector is another area where Tom's relationship-building and understanding of sales make him so successful. He is instrumental in finding winning partnerships with other organizations that also want to participate—publicly or not—in finding a cure. "Tom is in charge of corporate relationships and he's been extremely successful," Gary says.

We all know that every company has a different agenda or objective in treating, preventing or curing diabetes. Tom makes it clear that everyone can work together, and in DRI's spirit of collaboration, Tom makes it happen by asking two simple questions up front. "How can we work together and what's most important now?" These are the questions that get right to the heart of the matter so we can all help each other if there is some common ground. If there is common ground, Tom will find it, and like the BCTD, he will build on it.

That focused purpose has set in motion one of the most inspiring, encouraging and hopeful campaigns of learning and giving back, and is a true story of how one's deep passion and love for a child can turn into an unwavering commitment to improve their own lives, as well as the lives of others.

"DIABETES DAD" EMERGES

It is this body of Tom's work through speaking, writing, traveling to conferences, spending time with various organizations, meeting with other change agents, and truly understanding the diabetes world over time that has culminated in Tom being referred to as "Diabetes Dad." Realizing that many, many people know him by that name was an eye-opener for him. "That is such an awesome feeling," he says.

"We did not go into this thinking for one second that we would ever be in a position to help, but in sharing we have learned a lot," Tom says. "We have heard a lot, and I guess we have also helped as well. When a person came up to me once and asked, 'Are you Diabetes Dad?' it was all-telling that this journey, this diabetes movement is so much bigger than we could ever imagine."

I was once told that without humility there is no growth. It is the curiosity of learning, the desire to know more, the acknowledgment of not having all the answers that is so rare today and is a genuine part of Tom's character and what inspires others to do their best. He knows what he's doing and, especially, why he's doing it.

"When my kids get a break, so will I," he says defiantly. "Not one second before. If they can keep at it, and they do, my work is a piece of cake compared to what they have to deal with. It is not my disease, it is theirs. They can never stop thinking about it. I have to try to match that as much as I can even though I simply cannot, as I do not have it. I also work beside some of the most incredible people in the world. We cannot forget that point. I have seen people do incredible things with this disease and in spite of this disease, some well-known and some just kids doing their thing but doing it all *with* diabetes. That is not such an easy point to just look beyond."

This sentiment has also played out very strongly in Tom's advocacy and resilience. Tom has been steadfast and persistent in his philosophy and his actions. "We continue to learn," he says, "and then we help others with whatever it is we have learned. We are always looking for the best people and organizations to cure this disease."

Not even Tom can believe how his life has changed course. "I am a completely different person," he says. "I have no idea what I would be were it not for diabetes. I would have continued my acting career and with the amount of successes that were coming my way, it might have even turned out very much the way I would have hoped." Now, none of that matters. Tom has grown. "My only focus has been driven to help find a cure for my kids and the millions like them as well as look for opportunities to help those with diabetes."

When you talk to Tom, you come away feeling very empowered, inspired and motivated to do your part, whatever and however you define that for yourself. Tom realizes and appreciates that everyone's contributions are different, and he feels, as I do, that everyone needs to find out what that is for them.

In Tom's Words

"I have constantly said it is important to 'just don't do nothing.' I know so many people who have changed this world. The pain we all live with has surely given us enormous laughter, help, joy, knowledge, and most importantly, hope for all those who have diabetes."

Tom is also incredibly knowledgeable and candid about the political aspects of diabetes and has the urgency to get people working together and clear about what their goals are. "There is a lot of waste and people with personal agendas in this field of diabetes," he says. "If we collaborated more and looked for the synergies of what we have in common instead of why we are so different, I swear we would be so much further ahead in so many aspects of this disease."

Tom's focus as he represents all of us every day comes from a deep belief that we should keep striving for the day of a cure. "Managing the disease is so crucial for our children's survival, but better treatment means more money for the companies who make them," he says. "That's fine with me. If you create something that can really help manage diabetes better, you are entitled to that reward, but there are so many attempting different spins on a cure to get people to follow. There is management of the disease and there is a cure. People need to work diligently toward the goals and stop trying to blur the lines to pull at the desire that every parent wants for their child, a cure."

DIABETES POLICE AND THE NON-NEGOTIABLES

In the meantime, Tom marches forward. His kids are old enough to manage themselves these days, but he admits he's a real pain to them. "The 'diabetes police' is a title I wear proudly."

Tom refers to the diabetes police as any time a parent needs to really take control and set boundaries. Diabetes is a complex disease and is riddled with more riddles than answers. Some things are certain in the Karlya household. When it comes to caring for your child and looking out for their safety, there is no compromise. "In many households, I find that the parents are punishing the children for diabetes," Tom says. Making comments like "You could die younger" or "You will lose your feet" are examples of punishing someone for having diabetes. "In our home, it's not what diabetes will do to you which is long term, but rather, 'How are you feeling now?' and 'Do you want to feel better?'" Tom says. As you're reading this, you may intuitively know this doesn't always work by itself so that's where the diabetes police comes in. "My kids aren't punished for diabetes, they're punished for not listening," he says.

Tom's reasoning is simple, but effective: If you're managing the short-term aspects of treating diabetes, then the long-term consequences you're worried about simply won't happen. One of my favorite expressions that popped into my head as Tom was explaining this to me is to focus on your goals, not your fears. That's why the Karlya household has "non-negotiables"—the rules of parenting in your home—that don't consider diabetes separate from any other issue. As Tom reminds me, "Kids with diabetes are still kids." Here are a few of the non-negotiables in the Karlya home:

- Always wear your medical ID bracelet.
- Check in (call, text, email) at home if you're going to be late.
- Always test your blood glucose before you drive and before meals.
- Never text and drive.

So, what are the non-negotiables in your home? What are you punishing? Focusing on punishing the disease contributes to the ongoing burden of type 1 diabetes and creates more tension. Tom punishes *not listening*. It is just as important to wear your seat belt as it is to check your blood sugar before meals. While one has a clear diabetes component, Tom and Jill are not separating them. If you don't do what you're responsible for or what you have control over then that is what gets punished, just as in any non-diabetes home.

Just as important, Tom knows when not to be a cop and where trying to take control would backfire. "I can't speak from experience about having diabetes," he says. "I can speak from experience about a parent managing a child with diabetes, but I will never know what it's like to have it unless I get it." His message to me as a parent of a type 1 child, and now in these pages for all of us: "If you haven't experienced it, you can't argue it." I am so grateful that Tom is so emphatic about this and can look back on years of experience to assist those of us who are new or relatively new at this, trying to learn our way and cope with such a challenging disease.

IF YOU HAVEN'T BEEN THERE...

After Tom had spoken with trusted friends, doctors and others connected to type 1, he was excited to let Kaitlyn know that he heard insulin shots hurt less in the abdomen than where she had been giving herself injections. She wasn't buying it. He tried to explain it to her, shared his findings, pleaded with her. Still, she wasn't buying it.

One night when Tom and Jill's babysitter, who also has type 1, came to the house, Tom asked her a question. "Where do you give yourself shots?" "In the abdomen," she replied. He asked her to show Kaitlyn the next time she had to give herself an injection. Kaitlyn watched the babysitter calmly and without pause stick the needle into her abdomen. She was sold. Kaitlyn had just seen someone doing what she does each and every day, so it had a greater impact on her course of action. Then, Tom, in his amiable manner and a tone of wisdom over the years, referenced a scene from the movie, *Father of the Bride*. It is where the daughter will not listen to her dad (Steve Martin) to put a coat on. When her fiancé shows up, he advises her to put a coat on and she immediately does it. Certain people are in the best position to move us. We need to leverage that resource, not for manipulation, but because all of us need different people to influence us in ways that we find them credible.

There are times when Kaitlyn only wants to talk to Rob. Tom doesn't take that as him not being needed and he doesn't worry about trying to know everything. "Parents lose all the time because they haven't experienced diabetes." Tom's approach: There are shared experiences everywhere: Facebook group pages, LinkedIn communities, public events, camps, among many other options. If your child doesn't have a sibling with type 1 diabetes—and even if they do—it's important they find someone they can relate to from shared experience. There are times when Tom hears Kaitlyn and Rob talk about diabetes and he marvels at the connection and understanding, further realizing he has a clear role to play that doesn't include true empathy.

THE ART OF LETTING GO

Since Tom has never experienced diabetes, he also doesn't feel like he can ask his children about everything. I really believe this is a subtle distinction, but Tom's convinced me it's critical. "You just don't need to know about everything they're doing and what all their internal challenges are," he says. "Sometimes you just need to let go. As I've learned some things need to take care of themselves."

The key here is to know when that is needed. This is not easy, but worth gaining some awareness about. We can't hold on too tight. It creates additional worry and anxiety. It pressures those with type 1 diabetes already having to deal with living with this disease. It adds tension in our relationships at the same time it damages our health through stress hormones.

Trust and the art of letting go, I have come to appreciate (if not excel at), is a regular practice in our home. The first time Gavin had to go to school, Tara was extremely and understandably anxious. The preparation of food, the carbohydrate counting, the morning fixed routine could all be disrupted by a bad night's sleep or a particularly stressful day among many other variables. Tara takes the daily phone calls from school filled with the latest information and the possible consequences, and assimilates that all within 30 seconds to play doctor for her child. To pretend that doesn't add stress to your life is ignoring the reality. The way she has managed to deal with that is to let go more, to do the best she can and trust that he will be fine, and mostly, he is.

There is so much we all worry about—schools, nurses, excessive play, too much food, not enough sleep, getting sick and other people seeing low or high signs when we're not there. It all leads to a chronic state of anxiety that doesn't serve health or positive relationships. As Tom reminds me, we can't control it all so don't try to. Control the non-negotiables in your home, whatever they may be, and do your best to focus on consistent behavior to produce the best outcome, but not to obsess about each outcome.

~~~~~~

A Personal View: Life With an Asterisk

When I reflect on my son's diagnosis and subsequent daily campaign living with type 1, I feel so much love for who he is and what he puts up with. Gavin loves parks, loves to run and play, and loves to swing on the monkey bars after having watched his older brother, Jake, tackle them almost every day. Watching my boys play at the park and laugh is one of the greatest gifts for me. As I watch Gavin swing with focus and delight, I often think about the duality of emotion that stirs within me. At once, happy and relieved that this chronic disease is manageable while at the same time, saddened and angered that moments like these can often turn to rapid lows or just wondering how he's really feeling inside. I hear Tom's words in moments like this. "It is the stealing of the childhood that is the most frustrating. They have to grow up so much earlier due to all of the management they must do to stay alive."

What I realize now is not only how true that is, but I also realize the type of person that this will make him and at that, I can smile. And, so did these words from Tom:

"So, we watch in awe and can only begin to try and empathize, but we'll never truly know what it's like to live with this constant disease. We're heartbroken, frustrated and always trying to keep the seesaw from bouncing too hard. And, with all that, we can do nothing but watch in amazement at how our loved ones battle and deal every day with this disease."

Just after Halloween in 2011, at a museum, I was holding Gavin's hand walking around when he uttered his usual line associated with a low or high. "Dad, I don't feel OK." "OK, buddy," I said. "Let me check you so I can help you feel better." As I was giving him insulin to correct a blood sugar of 300, a woman had asked me if he had too much candy over Halloween. These kinds of things at one time would bother me, but I realize it is the lack of understanding. There are many misunderstandings about diabetes. Type 1 versus type 2, insulin dependent, why some people can take pills while others can't and many other aspects that most people really don't understand. That's fine, but what I do want people to know is how strong and determined type 1s are. I experience and feel Gavin's strength every time I watch him interact with others who will never know the daily pricks of a needle, and while of course it breaks my heart, it also has this wondrous effect of lifting me up as I see the gift of who he is and what obstacles he will overcome in his life.

"Diabetes is in everything and for them to achieve anything is a major accomplishment—they amaze me every day," Tom says. "Everything in Kaitlyn and Rob's life comes down to doing everything with an asterisk."

There is always more to the story that isn't seen on the surface.

TOM'S GREATEST ROLE

On birthdays, the Karlya family sits around the table and reads cards aloud.

It was Kaitlyn's birthday. Rob handed her his card and smiled. He knew the positive emotion that stirred within him when he wrote the card would be transmitted to her as well. She read the card and the words of gratitude, appreciation, understanding and love swept over her, too much to bear. Tears fell around the table.

Here's what the chronic disease of diabetes creates: empathy, trust, recognition, expressions of gratitude and appreciation for those in our lives who truly matter.

Here's a movie reference for Tom. In the movie, *People Like Us*, Chris Pine (Sam), the lead character, shares six rules for life success with his 11-year old nephew (Josh) played by Michael Hall D'Addario. "Rule number three," Sam says, "the things you think are important are unimportant, the things you think are unimportant are important." Most of all, this is what diabetes reminds us of every day.

I ask Tom if deep down he truly misses acting and how his new role has shaped his life. He answers in collective and team form about all the other advocates and people making a huge difference in the diabetes world. "It's a role that none of us wanted on a stage in life that none of us could avoid." He adds with the urgency of a family man on a mission: "I don't do anything halfway. I miss acting, but this is where I need to be right now. I'll get back to acting when we cure this." He is, after all, still a member of the Screen Actors Guild.

KAMAAL WASHINGTON

Co-creator, *Omega Boy versus Doctor Diabetes*
comic book series
Diagnosed in 2003 at age 9

~~~~~~

Omega Boy versus Doctor Diabetes

Omega Boy lunges back and kraks Dr. Diabetes across
the head! "No one made you have diabetes and you
have done nothing wrong. Your body is not producing
insulin, which makes your blood sugar too high. However, you don't have to be a villain. You can be a hero and
defeat diabetes," says Omega Boy.

~~~~~~

ON A FAMILY TRIP TO ST. LOUIS IN 2003, KAMAAL WASHINGTON
WAS complaining of constant thirst and feeling ill. Thirst to the
point of downing 42-oz. drinks back-to-back and still experiencing cottonmouth.

The trip, which involved six siblings, his mother, Dana, and
his comic book-writer and community activist father, Alonzo, had
been a purposeful one; a weekend of activities to bring attention
to a missing child case.

But when Kamaal began experiencing stomach cramps, making frequent trips to the bathroom and had numbness in his fingers, the immediate purpose of the trip was to get him to the emergency room.

That first blood check when something is wrong with your child is a moment burned into the consciousness as the JFK assassination or 9/11. You don't forget it. It's immediate and in the few seconds that determine the balance of your child's future and your own, this is a countdown like no other. Most meters take five seconds to give you this life-changing result.

For Kamaal, his number on this fateful day was 700 and he was immediately transferred by ambulance to the children's hospital. It was there they learned that Kamaal had type 1 diabetes. "I got really scared," Kamaal said. "I was wondering what would happen to me." It was a lot for anyone to handle, let alone a 9-year-old boy. He wasn't the only one. Dana's emotions and deep love for her son surfaced in a concoction of emotion that resonates with any type 1 parent. "It took a long time for me to come to terms with the diagnosis," she said. "Why is this happening to my child and why is this happening to us? I felt that I should have noticed it sooner or that maybe I could have done something to prevent it. That guilt just laid there for a while until I finally accepted that it would have happened regardless."

For his brother Malcolm there was complete fear. "When my brother was diagnosed I didn't know if he'd live or die. I didn't know if I was going to lose my brother that night." Their world crashing, tears and fear of the unknown boiled over with no way to contain it.

As they were discharging Kamaal and Dana knew the family was on its own, she broke down and asked the nurse, "How am I going to do this? I don't see how I can do this because it's just too much for him. He's too young for this to be happening to him." Little did she know her children would figure out a way to not only help Kamaal cope, but to help thousands of others as well.

When the Washington family arrived at the hospital, they entered into a boot camp on diabetes. One of the more ridiculous aspects of getting diagnosed with diabetes is that before you even internalize and assimilate what has happened, you have to enter an intensive training on how to survive to be released from the hospital as quickly as possible. It's like learning how to swim by getting tossed into the deep end. "There was no time for denial," said Alonzo, "only time to act."

Dana recalls this experience very well, particularly during the injection discussion. "For people who have never done any type of injection, just the thought of giving your child a shot, the needle pricks every day and the need to balance the insulin amounts just right. It was very, very frightening, even for me as an adult. But Kamaal handled it very well."

"I gave myself a shot in the hospital. It was something that I'd have to do for the rest of my life, so I just got used to it. I overcame my fear of needles right there," Kamaal said.

Fear and a fair amount of panic are necessary ingredients to help you overcome anything. Getting diagnosed with type 1 is a bombshell as Dana describes it, but she's also emphatic that it's OK to panic and it's OK to be afraid. You need it to mobilize yourself to face life's greatest challenges. You do what you have to do and those are the steps you need in order to overcome.

Acceptance came to Dana and Alonzo with clear roles to play in Kamaal's life. As the mother, Dana had the softer, more consoling role. Alonzo was more matter of fact. It was Alonzo who came up with the slogan, "You are not going to let diabetes overcome you. You are going to overcome diabetes." It was also Alonzo who knew they had to take action to battle this disease in a public way. Dana supported Kamaal on those days he just didn't want to deal with it. She would explain to Kamaal that she understood that there are days when you just want to be spontaneous like your siblings and to not always have to be monitoring yourself. She went on to suggest that the consequences of not staying with it would outweigh that "I don't care" feeling. Even more important, she held Kamaal's value and emotionally held him by explaining that it's OK to feel bad at times and go to the darker places in your mind about "Why me?" Her empathy pours into Kamaal and like a sponge, he accepts it, knowing that she has her moments where she wonders why her child would get this disease. The critical factor as Dana explains to me is that they don't stay there in what they call "Pity City." They step out and say, "We can do this" and get on with it. Both parents made it clear to their son that he was going to be healthy because they were going to help him learn to take care of himself and that this was not something to be afraid of.

Consider the ongoing demand with this condition. The children have to deal with this each day, constantly and with no let up. Within that context, the road and lessons to preparation, discipline and feeling proud of what you have to do just to show up every day are ever present. What most people never think about— blood sugar—these kids are monitoring regularly. Does that make you a stronger individual? Of course it does. Does the person who gets up at 5:30 in the morning to run or work out and is at work

30 minutes early in order to get the day started with a strong, proactive stance have a better chance to succeed? Yes, and if you're type 1, that mindset is required to not only succeed, but just to get to an even playing field.

As parents, we can be examples of a great way to live to be successful. Alonzo works out every day and he is mindful about healthy eating, and as a result, Kamaal strives to do the same things. He also pushes Kamaal. One of my favorite things he says to Kamaal is: "We live in Kansas City, not Pity City." He encourages him to do things, speak out, be unashamed, to overcome. "I began to eat healthy and work out every day to encourage Kamaal to do the same."

In addition to this personal and family triumph in turning a negative situation into a positive one lies one of the most remarkable aspects of their journey.

The books that the diabetes doctors gave Kamaal with big words and medical terminology weren't much help to him. So, when Malcolm, Kamaal's nearest younger brother, visited him in the hospital and noticed all the complicated books geared toward adults, he said, "We should do a comic book about this." After all, comic book writing is in the family. Their father writes the Omega 7 comic book series, which features super heroes who fight crime and keep their communities safe. And so, the groundbreaking "Omega Boy versus Doctor Diabetes" was born. The boys created a brilliant story to make it easy for kids to learn about diabetes and understand how to control the disease. "It's changed our lives," said Alonzo. The comic book also was the turning point in Kamaal's acceptance of this life-changing condition. He could fight it in a healthy way and even help others in overcoming the illness. Further, a chronic illness that brings most children sadness and makes them feel like an outcast became a way for Kamaal and Malcolm to gain national media attention.

The boys have sold and donated to diabetes groups about 90,000 copies of the comic and have given about half of their $135,000 in profits to diabetes causes. The message promoted in the comic book is that you can be a hero against diabetes, you can take a negative situation and make it positive.

Today, the young duo expresses their creative flair and advocacy in an unrelenting campaign surrounding diabetes awareness that is nothing short of astounding.

In addition to writing a diabetes superhero educational comic book that has swept the nation and brought them attention and speaking opportunities, Kamaal also served as a Children's Congress delegate for JDRF to testify before the U.S. Senate about diabetes research support.

CNN, *People*, Scholastic, *dLife*, The Associated Press and many diabetes publications have covered the boys. They even made the cover of a Beijing diabetes magazine. *The message heard around the world: Don't let the disease overcome you, you overcome the disease.*

They were recognized in 2006 with an enormous honor by *dLife* for those who make a difference against diabetes. With thousands voting online to name the top three winners, Kamaal and Malcolm were absolutely elated when their father gave them the news that they took first place. "It inspires us to do more," Malcolm said. Kamaal added, "We had to start smaller and we just keep hoping to raise awareness about diabetes."

It's that humility and passion that combine to power their dreams to grow. They continue to spread their message and have graduated to promoting healthy eating and safe driving in their comics. Both boys volunteer with their local JDRF and ADA chapters.

"Kamaal seems like a person who does not have a chronic illness. He is so active and happy. Beyond being a comic book creator, he is a skate boarder, rapper and break dancer as well," says Alonzo. "Diabetes is a part of his life that he controls. He has no shame or depression about the diagnosis. He has taken on the fight like a true super hero. Maybe, super heroes really do exist because he is defeating Dr. Diabetes every day."

Omega Boy versus Doctor Diabetes

As they shake hands in united triumph, Omega Boy speaks out to his former villain. "You're not a monster, my friend. You are just a child with an illness. With the right attitude and proper healthy choices you can be a super hero that conquers diabetes."

With the third comic book in production, their dialogue now is around creating their own animated series and producing a movie. "It will always have action and be fun to look at, but it will also be educational," Kamaal said. "We always want to have a message."

That is a message for a lifetime.

KELLI KUEHNE

Professional Golfer, Golf Analyst
Diagnosed in 1987 at age 10

NORMAL. WHAT IS NORMAL ANYWAY? WELL, AS DESCRIBED ON
www.dictionary.com, normal means "conforming to the standard
or the common type; usual; regular."

A NOT-SO-NORMAL FAMILY

By that definition, the Kuehne family is quite *abnormal*. Not in
the way we *normally* hear that word, but in a spectacularly positive, abnormal way. The kind of abnormal that has produced three
siblings, all incredible athletes who have a fire for competition and
selected golf as their sport. No, nothing in the Kuehne family is
normal. "I don't think my kids are competitive by accident," said
their dad, Ernie, a successful lawyer and businessman. All three
kids have won USGA championships, one of the most *unusual*
family accomplishments in all of sports.

Trip, Hank and Kelli Kuehne come from a storied golf family. Trip, born in 1972, finished second to none other than Ti-
ger Woods in the 1994 U.S. Amateur. He won back-to-back
Texas high school golf championships, a feat matched only by
Ben Crenshaw, Justin Leonard and Tom Kite. He also played on
three Walker Cup teams for the U.S. and was the lowest scoring
amateur in the 2003 U.S. Open. Trip now owns an investment
company.

Hank, born in 1975, earned All-American honors three times at Southern Methodist University, won the 1998 U.S. Amateur and became a PGA touring professional in 1999, also winning three Canadian Tour events.

Kelli, born two years later in 1977, recalls getting no special treatment for being the youngest of the bunch, let alone being the only girl. You get a sense just from talking to her for two minutes what kind of inner strength, confidence and commitment stirs her enthusiasm and joy for life.

"Everything they did, I did," Kelli says, referring to how she was always treated as an equal. The only rule she can remember from when the siblings were younger was that they couldn't block her in basketball because she was shorter. Wow, what nice older brothers!

Where some families may bond over vacations, church events, movie night, academics or meals, it was sports that fused and bonded the Kuehne family's togetherness into a unified molecule; separate atoms bouncing off walls, but contained in one molecular unit. Kelli's father was hard driving, but fair, even coaching their teams growing up, and as she attests, "laziness was not an option in our house." To help fuel balance and achievement, their mother, the one member of the family without the competitive bone, did just about everything else, including being cheerleader, cook and chauffeur as well as guardian of the family's emotional resilience (i.e., not taking everything too seriously and remaining calm in stressful situations).

I can only imagine in a family where you have three competitive, goal-oriented and aspiring professional athletes the kind of intense stressful environment that can emerge. It also takes a lot more than just sheer talent to play at the highest level of any sport.

What *is* clear is that without Mom's adept handling of grumblings over tournaments not quite played "up to par," mood swings and jittery nerves, it is very possible that the Kuehne family would not have produced three stellar athletes who achieved professional golf status.

FAMILY COMES FIRST

Values can be a defining force in our lives. They help guide us and inform life decisions, particularly when choices are difficult to make. Learning who we are and what we stand for grounds us and prompts us to make good decisions, especially when we're under pressure or when temptation arises. For many people, including myself, getting clarity on our values takes time and experience.

For Kelli, it was at the ripe old age of 8 when she first realized that family comes first, sports second. Playing national tennis, she was split up from her brothers and father one summer when they were pursuing golf at the very same time she was finding great success on the hard courts. One day as she was riding in the car with her "Momma," as Kelli calls her, she said, "You know, this sucks. I want to be with my family and spend more time with my brothers." So, in a split second, Kelli decided to give up a sport she was excelling at without knowing if she would like or even excel at golf. What she did know is that she wanted to be around her brothers more often. She also had a notion that she could play golf. "I knew I wanted to compete and I wanted to be around my family more so I had a strong feeling that golf would work out."

As Kelli describes her feelings, I can't help but marvel at the simple fact that she gave up something very promising for something unknown. At that age, when our identity is forming and people are telling you you're great, it must be hard to say, "OK, I'm going places in tennis, but it's not nearly as important to me as just spending more time with my family, especially my older brothers." Here's a little girl playing tennis at the national level, thinking of her family and wanting to pursue a different sport so she could grow up with her siblings, sharing a purpose and a passion. Kelli played her last tennis match at the age of 9 not fully knowing where her next jolt of competition would come from.

Her decision continues to have a very clear impact on Kelli to this day. For her, family comes first, sports second. No question, no doubt.

FOCUS, DETERMINATION, DRIVE

Right in the heart of McKinney, Texas, nestled in natural woodlands, sits Stonebridge Ranch Country Club. It features Pete Dye- and Arthur Hills-designed golf courses. Having one of them would be nice to call your country club. This stunning, family-oriented facility was named in the Best of Private Clubs 2011 list by *Avid Golfer Magazine*. It was there that Kelli began to realize that in addition to spending more time with her brothers, golf would be an excellent choice to stimulate her drive for competition and challenge.

"We used to hit balls into different buckets from 30 to 100 yards out," Kelli said. "We were trying to fly it into the bucket and that can be a great challenge." She added that their father was teaching them not to hit the same shot over and over. It developed their sense of feel and focus. The Kuehne children's putting competitions were full of fun and any gender differences that are related to how far one can hit a golf ball simply didn't exist. They would play in weekend games for money with other top members of the club, all 4-handicappers or less. It was not a lot of money, but enough to sharpen their focus and develop their skills under pressure. Kelli's father would tell their competition that if you took the kid's bet that they were responsible for paying. There was no bailing out in this family and it taught all of them a sense of responsibility and gave them a framework that helped to develop their emotional and mental strength on and off the golf course.

Kelli shares these memories with great delight and it's easy to see how golf won her over. "You can play every day and it's always something different," she says. Whether it is the course conditions or weather or what swing you have that day, it requires a great amount of focus, determination and drive. The game of golf is the kindling that lives inside Kelli, stoking her with happiness and fulfillment.

As a child, Kelli learned through individual sports—first with tennis and later, golf—that fulfillment comes from the inside out. Challenging yourself, striving for perfection (while knowing not to expect it), and pushing yourself to constantly improve—these qualities are instilled in Kelli. Golf became the perfect challenge for her because of its many facets and the relentless pursuit of improvement and perfection in a game that offers perfection to no one. And, so, at the age of 10, Kelli became the third Kuehne child to choose golf as her sport.

DEALING WITH DIABETES ... TOGETHER

It also turned out that there was another huge transition in Kelli's life at about the time she gave up the hard courts for the short grass.

Type 1 diabetes came on very suddenly for Kelli at the age of 10. For a healthy, active fifth grader playing multiple sports, it was odd, to say the least, to lose weight quickly despite a ravenous appetite. When Kelli's Momma saw her little girl drinking half-gallons of water at a time and it still wasn't enough to quench her thirst, she knew right away that something was amiss.

Being the voice of calm and reason, Momma Pam told Kelli that they were going to see a doctor to find out what was going on, and that she would take care of everything and always support her. "My mom is the essence of calm," Kelli says, "and I remember vividly to this day how my diagnosis was handled."

At the doctor's office, Kelli was peeing on a ketone stick. A ketone stick is a small, plastic strip with an absorptive end that is used to determine if ketones are present or if a person has diabetic ketoacidosis, a life-threatening condition in which the blood pH becomes extremely high due to formation of ketones. Ketones, in turn, form as a result of a lack of sufficient insulin in the body. Kelli had all the telltale signs of diabetes: thirst, excessive urination and weight loss. A blood sugar test of 376 confirmed the type 1 diabetes diagnosis. "Mom, am I going to die?" she asked. "No," her mom replied. "You are going to be fine. We're going to learn all we can about diabetes and we'll be OK, in fact, we'll be better than OK."

Again, this speaks directly to how our emotions influence others profoundly, as energy is contagious. As parents, we have inordinate influence by virtue of our role. By controlling our emotions and staying in the moment (as Kelli's mother did when Kelli was diagnosed), it shows us that we all have a choice to make about how we teach our children and others to manage difficult circumstances. Calm and collected, Pam's message to Kelli was clear: This is a situation to be dealt with, and while it's not welcome, it's here. We will figure it out. Distress and anxiety will hamper us so we will deal with this together; you're not alone. There is nothing we can't overcome as a family.

A Personal View: Embrace It

It's not pretending that nothing matters or putting your head in the sand, it's a matter of keeping perspective and doing the best we can, knowing we will always be there for the ones we love. One parent that I spoke with after his 5-year-old daughter was diagnosed told me that he cried twice in the hospital on their initial stay. The reason? On both occasions he saw children with cancer and that immediately rocked him to perspective. "Of course, this is not something we wanted, but I think of that all the time when I feel beat up by this disease," he said.

Kelli's initial reaction to her diagnosis was, as it is for most of us, fear-based. Am I going to live? How will my life have to change? Can I still achieve my dreams? Will I be treated or looked at differently? We all ask these questions, whether you are diagnosed or someone you love is diagnosed. We also all must go through the necessary stages from awareness to acceptance, and from what I've learned, another key stage in this evolution for those that have truly mastered type 1 is embracing. Yes, embracing.

How can you embrace such a chronic and challenging condition? Well, from talking to Kelli and countless others who are living exceptional lives with type 1, it is clear to me that this is the critical piece. "How can you not?" is my question. Accepting is saying OK, I have this and I need to deal with it. In a sense, it is a passive state of being. Embracing suggests action. As Tim Robbins said in the great movie *Shawshank Redemption,* "You can get busy living or get busy dying."

YOU HAVE A CHOICE

With the support of her family and their implicit and explicit commitment to her, Kelli's evolution was rapid. It was clear to her before she left the doctor's office that the message was pretty simple. "You either take care of yourself and you'll be fine or you don't and you won't," she recalls the doctor saying. Although she was only 10 at the time, that message stuck with her for the next 25 years as she went on to become a professional golfer with 26 top 10 finishes on the LPGA tour, then became a mother herself. She knew she was going to live if she took care of herself. In fact, she knew that she could do everything she ever wanted as long as she was mindful of her diabetes. We all *know* what's good for us; it's the *doing* that separates the pack. Kelli recalls her parents telling her that if you want to make it happen, go make it happen. Don't play the victim. Anything you want, you can achieve. "I meet kids all the time that are angry and discouraged by diabetes," she says. "They are terrified of the unknown." In this scenario, choosing to be empowered also has a catch, as Kelli explains. "I never really had an excuse. I was never treated any differently so with that came the fact that I couldn't get out of anything." Kelli wants people to understand that those with type 1 diabetes have a choice to be empowered and to take responsibility. "It was very black and white for me," she says. "For kids, the choice to take responsibility and overcome can really make a huge difference because, as kids, they are even more adaptable to change. It gets harder the longer you go or the older you are to break out of bad habits."

In Kelli's Words

"Diabetes is a condition, it's not an excuse."

A FAMILY AFFAIR

Kelli also realized quickly that it wasn't just her who had diabetes, but that it was a family diagnosis. Her mother is from east Texas and is a Southern cook, so she basically had to relearn how to cook. The family quickly changed around Kelli's needs. Meals changed from heavier dishes loaded with carbs to more chicken, squash and broccoli. In one family moment, their father said, "This is how it's going to be." While not easy, especially for teenage boys, they knew it needed to be done. And they did it. That is the kind of support and commitment that propels any individual to stardom, not just those with type 1.

Her brothers, despite their initial fear and concern for their little sister, quickly adapted and willingly committed to understanding type 1 diabetes. For example, they began to learn the symptoms and patterns that Kelli would develop before lows. Kelli was bilingual (in Spanish and English) by the time she was in fifth grade. Hank began to notice something unusual that Kelli would do and it wasn't long before the family connected it to predicting a low blood sugar. Kelli would begin to speak in sentences of mixed English and Spanish. When this happened, her brothers knew to get her something to eat or drink because she likely was getting low. "Kelli's talking Spanish again, Mom," Hank would say. And with that, her blood sugar would be checked, although everyone knew that it was guaranteed to be low. They also began to notice how she would begin to sweat or her face would become paler. Type 1 diabetes was a family affair and this family rallied around Kelli to help her through this condition. The message over and over became clear for a young girl battling a chronic disease: "You're not alone."

It's also clear that a huge part of Kelli's work ethic and understanding of managing her condition is that her parents were not enablers. They provided her with everything she could possibly need to make good choices and learn how to manage her diabetes, but she was also empowered to be self-sufficient, capable and responsible for taking care of herself.

One of Kelli's most important messages is that it's great to have people on your side doing everything they can to support you, but in the end you have to make the choices and you know best about your own condition. Kelli was able to take on more of her own care at an early age because her parents and family expected that. Her independence and self-sufficiency combined with strong family support created a resilient, confident and proactive superstar. While it may seem counterintuitive, kids with diabetes whose parents teach them to be resilient, confident and proactive gain an advantage over other children who are shielded, protected or coddled because of their condition. Kids with diabetes, like Kelli, learn an invaluable lesson about being autonomous that can serve them well for the rest of their lives.

A Personal View: Why Me?

One of the biggest challenges for young people, be it tots, teens or young adults, is overcoming the "Why me?" syndrome. Kelli talks about this with great emphasis. "You just have to change your mindset," she explains. Kelli has a strong faith and feels strongly that God would not give type 1 diabetes to anyone who couldn't handle it. In fact, she believes if you have type 1 you have a responsibility to do something with it.

For those who may not be as spiritually inclined, it still is a matter of a strong belief in that sense of responsibility. In my son's case, I know that he will be better because of diabetes and in his unique way will do something with that sense of responsibility. I'm not referring to this sense of responsibility in taking on some larger-than-life mission either. What I've learned from both Kelli and our own experience is that it is about taking pride in who you are and doing what's necessary to take care of yourself so you can fulfill your dreams and passions. Tara and I can see it at the age of 5 when Gavin asks to be checked if he's not feeling right or at times before play. That's about as responsible as he can be right now, but I know that his spirit and attentiveness to managing his own life will take greater shape as he grows. For everyone, that will be different, but I agree that you must do something with your diabetes, even if it is just rising above it.

Kelli recognizes that type 1 is harder on the people who are not directly diagnosed. "It was much harder for my parents than it was for me. I realize that even more now that I have a baby girl." She may be concerned that her own daughter will get type 1 diabetes, but she's not afraid and she will do what's necessary if that happens—just what Ernie and Momma did for her.

Professional sports are a dream of many and a dream realized by a select few. I recall wanting to be a professional "anything" when I was younger and even though I excelled in many sports, I was never good enough at one thing to pursue it. I always imagined just how tough it must be to put in all those hours and sacrifice a normal (there's that word again) life. To reach that goal with type 1 diabetes is simply remarkable and incredulous. After winning successive amateurs and her later success on the LPGA tour, Kelli is happy to lead a not-so-normal life. In fact, after hearing about this family, who wants to be normal anyway?

~~~~~~

A Personal View: Become a Diabetes Ambassador

If you have type 1 diabetes, you have a choice: You can become its victim, or you can become its ambassador. Your choice is influenced by your beliefs about and understanding of this condition. If you believe that nothing you did (or didn't do) caused you to get type 1 diabetes, and that there was no way for you to prevent getting diabetes, you're on your way to using your condition to teach and support others. To recognize that you did not cause it and could have done nothing to prevent it (as there is still no known cause) is an important part of the mindset to escape victimhood and become an ambassador. Kelli's challenge to you: See what you can do with it.

"The only mistake is not doing anything about it," she says. Educate, inspire, lead, or just do the best you can—it will change your experience. As a result, it will change your life. I love that challenge because if you're not motivated to do it for your parents or loved ones, do it for yourself. Be who and what you always wanted to be in spite of *and* because you have type 1 diabetes.

I realize that this is not always easy because there are many forces of the type 1 experience that can put pressure on any type 1 individual: fear, overprotective and anxious parents, feelings that they did something to get it or that there is something different or wrong with them. In most of my conversations with people with type 1, rebellion from demanding or expectant parents becomes a reason to push back and not take care of your diabetes. Here's my question. Who is that pushback really hurting? We all know that what might come across as controlling or annoying is a result of someone caring deeply. Keep that in mind, share what it is that your loved ones do that creates the conflict and friction inside you and get on with it. They just want you to be healthy and seek a life with meaning. Diabetes may be there, but it's not in the driver's seat.

CAUSE AND EFFECT: MAKING ADJUSTMENTS

"Having diabetes prepared me for the rest of my life," Kelli says. "The biggest thing I learned and applied to my life was understanding cause and effect." From an early age, Kelli had to learn to make adjustments that other kids did not. She knew that eating a half of a peanut butter and jelly sandwich would bring her blood sugar up about 100. She also knew an apple would have a similar effect. This was all trial and error, learned by frequently checking her blood sugar. The other aspect of diabetes that prepared her was paying attention to how her body felt. "I know that my lips and tongue start to go numb and my fingers start to tingle when my blood sugar level is dropping," she says. "I get cottonmouth and feel groggy when it's elevating. What I learned as a little girl still applies today in that I know how to offset the lows and highs before they happen so I can focus on what I need to do to perform." For Kelli, it's really about paying special attention to the obstacles in your life and figuring out how to systematically overcome them.

Kelli applies the same logic and discipline to golf. "Cause and effect," she says. "If I keep missing a shot left on the course, I know it is because I am most likely too shallow and flippy with my left wrist. So I make adjustments. I work on getting the angle of my swing path more vertical and work on keeping a really neutral and straight left wrist to avoid hitting the same left ball."

Kelli has learned that in life, it's absolutely necessary to course-correct whether on the course or off. Having that flexibility, patience and determination has enabled her, a consistent top performer on the golf course, to play at the highest level of sports as well as manage her diabetes like a pro.

It also proves to me that with the right support, mindset, tools and commitment, type 1 diabetes can take you the extra mile because you know what it takes to make adjustments, be prepared, be disciplined and be proactive just to have a chance at your dreams. "If you take control now, you'll have a lot less work to do in the future," Kelli says. These words of wisdom could serve us all well. The fierce intentionality required for consistent positive behaviors means that we have to make them automatic. Since so much of what we do is automatic anyway, then our success in managing type 1 diabetes will be in direct proportion to how automatic those healthy behaviors become.

Kelli Kuehne is not just a great golfer; she is a great advocate and responsible person who also happens to have type 1 diabetes. It is not who she is, but she doesn't hide it and she will always take the time to educate and be a role model for others. Having raised more than $2 million for diabetes causes and sporting her insulin pump not far from her golf glove, she is the embodiment of what happens when you embrace a would-be obstacle and turn it into a driving force.

"Being diagnosed with diabetes taught me a discipline and patience well beyond my 10 years of age at the time," she says. "It also taught me perseverance and that nothing could stand in the way of my dreams. I aspired to be a professional golfer at 12 years old. The idea never occurred to me that I wouldn't make that a reality. I still carry that with me today. It's a way of life for me."

Now, at age 35, happily married with a 4-year-old girl, she has reached the next stage of her life after deciding not to play professionally anymore. Kelli will stay closely connected to the game as a guest analyst for the Golf Channel. The role is perfectly suited for her given she was a radio and TV broadcasting major at the University of Texas. "I have always wanted to stay involved in the golf world after I retired from playing competitively." With her professional life moving triumphantly ahead, she's more focused on her current threesome that may just become a foursome. She's every bit as excited talking about her family as she is her golf career, and with her father's competitive fire that still burns deeply inside her, she speaks with her mother's calmness and poise: "My family will always come first, always."

RICH HOLLENBERG

Sportscaster
Diagnosed in 2006 at age 35

When I first found out that one of my closest friends in the world had type 1 diabetes, I was shocked. First, I knew little about the disease other than that another close friend's daughter was diagnosed with it not long before, but she was barely 2. I didn't realize that this happened to 35-year-old adults. This was juvenile diabetes, wasn't it?

We were with another close friend of ours at his house enjoying an outdoor springtime barbecue in River Vale, N. J., when Rich gave us the news about his diagnosis. He had been living in St. Petersburg, Fla., for some time now, and I was living in New York City at the time, so I hadn't seen him in a while. From the moment I saw him that day, I knew something was not right. My image of Rich was always as a strong and healthy guy with a fun and outgoing personality. He looked different and he was different. This was a man who, until confronted with some back trouble, had participated in multiple sports, liked to run and bike, played outdoors with his kids, and hit the gym on a regular basis. Even with some chronic pain, he managed to do what he wanted to do and enjoy his life without a complaint, his kids and his family never truly knowing the pain he was in.

What I always have valued about our friendship is our mutual philosophy about embracing life and being the best you can be. Rich has always been doing what he has wanted to do—sportscasting. I remember during our senior year at Syracuse University, he would be at the main table in our apartment first thing in the morning preparing his voice, and practicing run-throughs of sport scores. "The Sabres topple the Devils 2-1, it was the Bulls running away from the Heat 101-80." So it went on most mornings in our small, but prized apartment on Comstock Road right across the street from our fraternity. He has stayed true to who he is and what he set out to do more than anyone I know. It wasn't always easy, either. He had many times where he could have called it quits, whether it was working far from home in Montana or having difficulty getting an agent that would take him seriously and truly understand his drive and talent.

When you know someone for this long, someone with whom you've built a deep and long-lasting relationship, it's hard to see them go through any pain. I saw pain and I was worried about my friend. I didn't know all that was ailing him, but it seemed clear to me that it was physical and emotional in nature. But knowing him, I knew that he would bounce back, that this would be a minor roadblock on his road to stardom doing what he loves to do. As you know, I learned then and know all too well now that diabetes is a roadblock every 30 yards like speed bumps in a neighborhood—always there, always a reminder.

With a few connections to my own family and friends with type 1 diabetes, I felt it was extremely important to hear from one of them directly. I enjoy being the purveyor of some of these amazing stories in this book, but I simply don't know what it is like to live with it. I have a better sense of empathy around type 1 diabetes, having to essentially manage it for someone else, but that is a far cry from walking in those shoes. As a result, I asked Rich to write about his experiences with type 1 diabetes, particularly since most of his life he didn't have it. Rich has had type 1 diabetes for only about one sixth of his life. It's that drastic change of suddenly having to manage a disease in the midst of a busy life of travel, family and community obligations that is so inspiring to hear someone rise above.

I could barely speak. Not from nerves. Not even from stress, although I carried around more than enough of that. "Laryngitis," I thought, dejectedly. It was August, 2006, and of all nights, the night I was set to interview a football legend—Joe Montana. Yes, *that* Joe Montana. And I could barely speak! You see, I make my living primarily with my voice, as a TV sportscaster, and now, on the verge of a personal and professional highlight, to say the least, my voice—the most significant asset in my occupational tool box—betrayed me. In front of a national TV audience, what was to be a career milestone would instead turn into a mockery.

I couldn't hide this one. Joe—anyone, for that matter—would hear it the moment I opened my mouth to speak. My other symptoms were easier to mask, especially to people who didn't see me on a regular basis: the rapid weight loss (30 pounds in six weeks), due in large part to my seemingly unquenchable thirst, which precipitated my maddeningly frequent trips to the bathroom to urinate. Even my blurred vision would go unnoticed by most people. I could handle these inconveniences. I could work around them. But, damn. I needed my voice to do my job.

Looking back, it was my Dad, of all people, who first diagnosed me with diabetes. He is not a doctor, mind you, but he put the pieces together. Incredulously, my primary care physician misdiagnosed me as a type 2 on my initial visit with the aforementioned symptoms and the subsequent blood work. After consulting with an endocrinologist shortly thereafter, who accurately diagnosed me as having type 1 diabetes, I was able to go back and look at the evidence to trace a timeline that led me to where I was at that point: That past December, I herniated two discs in my lower back, and when physical therapy didn't alleviate any of the pain, I turned to a cortisone injection. While the epidural instantly cured me of my back pain, the steroid ratcheted up my blood sugar. Turns out, the collateral damage was done, and permanently so. My pancreas, already stressed, but at the time showing no outward signs of breakdown, couldn't recover. From that moment, the thirst, the urination, the weight loss, and the impaired vision were like dominoes quickly falling in succession as my pancreas virtually shut down. On this one particular night, my voice went with it.

Even though I didn't know it at the time, the peripheral effects of diabetes (in this case, dehydration), coupled with the stress I was feeling from these undiagnosed symptoms (as well as other personal issues), conspired to take out a most necessary and required aspect of my job as an interviewer: my ability to speak. In retrospect, this episode shines a light on what is so infuriating about dealing with diabetes in general. It can affect different people in different ways, because it affects so many different aspects of your physiology and overall health: Your eyes, your mouth, your feet. In this particular case, my need for constant hydration went unheeded and my voice gave out.

Turns out, I'd recover enough that August night to salvage my interview with Joe Montana, but I would never recover from the hand I'd been dealt. There was no turning back from the fact that I had diabetes.

A LIFE-CHANGING DIAGNOSIS

I wasn't angry as much as I was lost. From the frustration of not knowing what was wrong with me, to the mishandling of my diagnosis (I was taking metformin, a pill used for type 2 diabetes, for months before I learned it was doing nothing for me), to the realization that my life as I knew it was forever altered. I was in a tailspin. Depression had set in. I didn't admit it then, but I know it now. My medical condition had adversely affected all aspects of my existence. My personal life was in turmoil, and I was in an extremely negative place emotionally.

I am no different from most other people—juggling family, a career, etc. But my situation felt like it was being pulled to the extremes. My career was moving along, but not in the fashion or the vein I had planned. I wasn't truly following my passion to be a sportscaster. I was on TV, but that wasn't fulfilling for me. Also, the hours I was working were really affecting my family time. One day I would be working during the daytime; the next, an overnight shift; after that, primetime hours. A lack of sleep was dragging me down. This was right around the time we were expecting our second child. As you can imagine, it was extremely taxing, handling the pressure of being a "public figure" on television, trying to be the best Dad I could be to my nearly-2-year-old son, expecting my first daughter. Something had to give, and my relationship with my wife was showing signs of cracks. I took a great deal of my frustrations out on her, and our marriage suffered because of my behavior and my condition.

Did diabetes play a role in my vulnerable state? I believe so. And I now know, from speaking with other people who have diabetes, that some degree of depression can be directly and indirectly attributed to the disease. Looking back, it was a general malaise that permeated my daily routine. My diagnosis and the ensuing months were met with ambivalence. I was essentially sleep-walking through life.

On a side note, I've never spoken about this, but for as long as I can recall, I remember thinking that someday I'd be stricken by something traumatic. When I was diagnosed as having diabetes, therefore, it seemed to make sense to me on some metaphysical level. Another negative thought that preyed on my vulnerability at the time: This disease was the payback for prior sins. I was being punished for the bad things I'd done in the past.

I didn't know a thing about diabetes prior to my diagnosis. Actually, I knew one thing: Wilford Brimley was the face of diabetes. But I soon discovered I was not as much of an anomaly as I'd thought. Still, as the resignation and reality of it all set in, I not only had to worry about how I would be affected day-to-day, I also had the additional concern for my children: Does this mean they are more susceptible to it? I quickly learned that diabetes was a disease of *meticulousness.* It would be the mundane rituals—the finger pricks; the insulin injections; the carb-counting—that take its toll.

Thankfully, I have the support of a loving and caring wife, not to mention my family and friends, who are always there. Now, every time I get a positive result from an A1C test, the first thing I do is text the good news to my wife, parents and my best friend (whose name is on the cover of this book).

Ironically, it is that ritualistic behavior that in some strange way dovetails with how I usually function. I am a creature of habit who works most efficiently when faced with a structured diagram of tasks or goals. I am a list maker (and a Virgo, if you subscribe to the astrological bent of things). So doing all the things I now had to do to live with diabetes added another element of *routine* to my existence. It also heightened my sense of pursuing a proper diet and a good balance of exercise, two things I thought I was already mindful of, but now had to be even more vigilant about.

I was hard on myself when I forgot to take my insulin pens and needles with me when I left the house. I cursed myself for not having the right kind of snacks on hand when my blood sugar dropped dangerously low, and I was left scrambling for the closest thing I could get my hands on, nutrition be damned. Another thing I noticed was how hard it was on my parents. They were in a sense of denial when I was first diagnosed, which was further exacerbated by the honeymoon phase (after the body starts utilizing glucose once type 1 has been established, some remaining islet cells may begin to recover the ability to produce insulin) I experienced, like so many type 1s go through when they first start taking insulin. Was it the cortisone? Was it the stress? Was it the lack of sleep? Did all of these elements conspire to create an illusion of diabetes that would vanish as quickly as it reared its ugly head? Sadly, no. My parents tried to convince themselves that my condition was reversible, and that somehow, despite an accurate diagnosis, I would at some point be able to go back to the way of life I led before any of this happened. No pens, no needles, no blood draws, no doctor visits. I think they were hoping it was more "environmental"—a result of external forces (lack of sleep, stress, etc.)—when in fact, it was not. My diabetes was here to stay.

A NEW ROUTINE

I can honestly say I came to deal with my future as a person with diabetes as I have with other major elements of my life: on my own terms. Yes, I am blessed to have a loving and devoted family, and friends who stand by me, and I would never discount the support they provide. But I tend to be fiercely independent—to the point of being introverted—when it comes to making decisions of major import. I never want to burden anyone with *my* problems or issues. I can handle it on my own. I approached all of my life-altering moments in similar fashion: choosing a college, a career, a wife. In that way, my personality had predetermined how I was going to come to grips with this curveball I was thrown. Deal with the facts. Move forward.

Once I accepted diabetes as something I'd live with possibly for the rest of my life, the bitter resignation I'd initially felt turned to dogged determination. I took steps to drastically improve my personal life for the better, and used my already existing trait of self-reliance as a positive force instead of something that could potentially prevent me from accepting help and support. My new typecast was beginning to take shape.

I've always taken relatively good care of myself, but now being in good shape was much more than an "ego" thing: I *needed* to be in good shape. In light of that, I accomplished a personal goal of competing in my first triathlon, determined to set an example for my children and myself. It also dawned on me that I could use my career status in television as a platform to help raise diabetes awareness. I soon became involved in my local ADA chapter, as a member of their executive committee. I am actively involved in the Step Out Walk and the Tour de Cure, the ADA's two major fundraisers. Whether it's making TV appearances on behalf of the ADA or lending my voice to fundraising calls, I am committed to being an active participant in the cause.

GAINING CONTROL

Presently, my diabetes is so ingrained in my everyday life that, after five years, it's almost an afterthought. Don't get me wrong: It still exists in the back of my mind, and there is still the requisite anxiety every few months when I visit my endocrinologist to get a report on my A1C (6.4 when I last checked!), but this is my reality, and I embrace the challenges that come with it.

My current perspective is, and has been, simple: Avoid the pump. I want to stress this is a very personal thing for me. I know many a person with diabetes who needs it and swears by it. This is not a referendum of anyone or any device. But for me, the ability to manually control my blood sugar with injections is a symbol of control. As long as I can keep the number of units I administer to myself to a minimum before each meal and at bedtime, I choose to live this way. As a result, in some small way, each day becomes a tangible victory for me. Additionally, I fall into a classification of diabetes sometimes known as having type 1½, so I am largely able to control the amount of insulin I need by diet and exercise. It also levels out my highs and lows with regard to blood sugar, and generally makes me feel better.

I am by no means perfect. This is the harsh reality of having type 1 diabetes. It will never go away unless a cure is found (hopefully). I can do everything exactly so and I will still battle the ups and downs of blood sugar management, and the frustrations that come with its inexactitude. And it's with that in mind that I will continue to push myself to be more vigilant about monitoring my blood sugar. I will constantly renew my energies to get in better shape. I will dig into whatever reserves I have when things don't go the way I want them to. This is about me, but it also about my family and the diabetes community that serves as a constant reminder that, although only I can be in charge of my situation, I am never alone in my struggle.

That brings me back to Joe Montana, of all people. There's something I've learned throughout my career in sportscasting, after gleaning nuggets of inspirational information from legends of the game like Joe, and many others. The parallels exist between the pressures and adversity they face on the field, and what we face in dealing with diabetes.

Either you control it or it controls you.

ROBERT CAMPBELL

Vice President of Innovation
and Product Research at Insulet
Diagnosed in 1977 at age 7

Diabetes, meet Rob Campbell.

An unusual thing happened when Rob was diagnosed at the age of 7: Type 1 diabetes got weaker.

It took time, but to all those who care about this disease you can take comfort in the fact that on March 14, 1977, on a dreary day in Hebron, Maine, of all people, type 1 diabetes chose Rob. Today, he is changing lives of type 1 diabetes patients as one of the creators of Insulet Corporation's OmniPod insulin pump, the only integrated, wireless and tubeless pump on the market.

Hebron, with a population of roughly 500, is in the "middle of nowhere," as Rob puts it. He grew up as a country boy. When you grow up in the country, it's not surprising that you'd have a passion for nature and a strong appreciation for our environment.

As Rob enjoyed the outdoors, animals and wildlife, protecting the environment became a passion at an early age. As I thought about how he would later in life also look to take care of people, it was clear to me that Rob Campbell is one of the few people who is truly driven by an internal mission to make lives better for others.

While this is very counter to our self-concerned society today, I believe it sets a strong example that we can all excel and be successful when we are grounded in values and look to give more than we get. The great motivational speaker Zig Ziglar is famous for saying, "To get what you want, help others get what they want." Rob has everything he needs and more, and not once did he think about what he would get out of his choices. He knew that by doing what he was passionate about and by putting others first, he would get all he needed.

Rob was like most any country boy prior to his type 1 diagnosis: He played outside with friends, finding his own games and enjoying nature. I am about Rob's age and we can attest to those early days in video games (Atari, Intellivision) that they didn't have enough intrigue to keep you inside like the computers, PlayStations, iPads and apps available today. While Rob had a strong creative predisposition and was interested in the sciences, he was equally, if not more, interested in sports. His parents must have known their child was very special when they saw that kind of balance.

Rob remembered a snowmobiling trip with his aunt and uncle prior to his diagnosis. "My uncle would later recall that I just kept tapping him on the back while we were riding to go to the bathroom," Rob said. A short time later, his mother, Betty, noticed that he was lethargic and not acting like himself.

A Personal View:
Actions Speak Louder Than Words

When Rob told me that his mother had noticed, just prior to his diagnosis, that he wasn't acting like himself, it really struck me. That's how my wife, above all, noticed that Gavin was not OK. He wasn't acting like himself.

This is such a strong sign of diabetes as much as urination or hunger and parents need to be aware of it. You know your child's personality and type 1 will rob them of it. One of the happiest days of my life is when Tara and I saw our child come back, when insulin began to swim in his bloodstream, unlock his cells and do its magic.

A STORMY, FATEFUL DAY

With those symptoms, Rob's mother took him to the Central Maine Medical Center in Lewiston on a stormy spring day. Rob remembers the strong rains and flood conditions that day and how difficult it was to get to the hospital.

Unlike now, Rob and his mother had to leave and wait for any news about what might be wrong. There were no test strips, instant glucose readings from a meter or thin gauge lancets. We received our diagnosis about Gavin in a matter of minutes, which is not only something we take for granted today, but provides newly diagnosed patients immediate care at a time when it is most needed. Rob, still feeling sick, left the hospital without a diagnosis.

Several hours later, Betty got a call from the doctor. Rob's blood sugar was in the 800s. So, there they were: A mom and her very sick child going back out into the storm, not knowing if the roads to the hospital were passable. As most parents do, Betty found a way.

MAKING A DIFFERENCE

While we don't know much yet about the triggers for type 1, we are beginning to learn about the potential roles that viruses, hygiene and formulas might play. What we know for sure, though, is it can seemingly strike anyone regardless of age, ethnicity, background, history or lifestyle. That is what is so perplexing. There are so many variables and uncertainties that finding a consistent source of the disease is incredibly onerous and complex.

With the rapid growth in cases over the last several years, a projected 1.3 million every year and growing, it's only a matter of time before it strikes certain people with the knowledge and resources to eventually defeat it. Never underestimate the power of love or family to make amazing things happen.

Here is where the diagnosis of another Rob intersects with the story of Rob Campbell, combined with the good fortune of a devoted family with vast resources to effect real, lasting change. To this story, we can also add the power of a knowledge economy with rapid advances in technology that made amazing things take shape. It did require, however, the randomness of who gets the disease to set the stage.

In 1992, 16 years after Rob Campbell was diagnosed, type 1 randomly selected another Rob. This Rob was 3-year-old Rob Brooks, whose father was a highly successful medical executive. Again, type 1 diabetes got weaker.

This is the kind of randomness that gives me goose bumps. The two Robs would forever be linked in the overarching mission to better manage type 1 diabetes. Put simply, when Rob Brooks was diagnosed, it set in motion one of the most significant advances that type 1 diabetes would see in modern times.

This would also take some time, but Rob's father, John L. Brooks, is another person in whom we can all take comfort, because he is operating in the world with a dedicated mindset to improve and ultimately cure the disease that plagues his son and millions more like him.

John's background as a medical executive is staggering. He co-founded three life sciences companies and, among other things, is a co-founder of Prism VentureWorks, which has raised more than $1.25 billion in capital.

When John was faced with his son's diagnosis, he began looking for a diabetes management solution in pump therapy. He recognized that his ambitions were far greater than what was available to him on the market. John's recognition did not thwart him, but mobilized a response filled with hope, promise and commitment to find a better way.

In 2000, John L. Brooks proceeded with $1 million to fund Insulet Corporation in what he believed could help fulfill his mission: a better way for people with type 1 diabetes to manage their condition. Twenty-four years after Rob Campbell was diagnosed and eight years after Rob Brooks was diagnosed came the opportunity that would change both their lives in dramatic ways.

LIVING THE DREAM

Rob Campbell always knew what he wanted to do. He's the kind of person who I can't help but admire and respect in so many ways. There's also something hugely energetic about people who have an unequivocal conviction about who they are and what they stand for. Rob has had type 1 diabetes for more than 37 years and he told me he's living a dream. What? How is that possible? In a world where people find the smallest things to complain about, this guy is telling me, in the most authentic and sincere way, that despite a chronic disease that he has to put in its place every minute of every day, that he is living a dream.

To understand how any of that makes sense you need to understand how Rob was brought up. His family had to deal with type 1 at what could be called a more primitive time for the disease.

I am convinced that while many of us remain steadfast in our quest and hope for a cure, managing type 1 today is a blessing compared to 1977. You want to hear a more empowering story about having type 1 today? Everything about type 1 care today didn't exist for people back then. No instant blood sugar readings; instead, retrospective glucose results based on urine samples. No Humalog, Novalog, Apidra, Levemir or Lantus, only animal insulins such as pig or beef. Scientists are still not happy with how slow insulin is today compared with how the body's beta cells release it. Imagine life only using trains before planes were invented except *this is your life support*. You could not be nearly as free as you are today with what you eat, how often you eat and even when you eat. Meal plans weren't an option, they were a necessity to take as much guesswork out of a pure guessing game. I am amazed when I hear about these challenges. I often marvel at how you can do something so often every day and still not always get it right. How did Rob's parents feel back then with not having all of the information, the technology and support that give us some vision in a blind sport? The chronic burden we share today must have been magnified 100 times. Some of the best means ever to assist us in playing doctor every day were simply not available. You just had to make do with animal insulin and old information. As Rob says today, "Frequent hypos were the norm. You just had to be prepared and educate those around you."

Rob was also raised with a keen understanding that diabetes took a back seat to him just being a kid. It reminds me of a great saying I heard from another type 1 individual: *I have diabetes, but diabetes does not have me.*

His parents pushed him to live a life where anything would be possible. Rob, to this day, credits his parents for this philosophy, by which he continues to live his life. "My parents could have easily said not to do certain things and really try to control every moment of my life and be overly rigid. But, they didn't and for that not only am I eternally grateful, but I am who I am today because of it," he says.

***

In Rob's Words

"That's what I learned more than anything from an early age. Be prepared."

***

There's a difference between setbacks and obstacles. That difference may be in perception, but that takes us back to how important the stories are that we tell ourselves. An obstacle is a hindrance to advancement. A setback connotes moving backward. Having type 1 feels like an ever-present burden to many people because a) it never goes away; b) it is a major issue to deal with that has significant repercussions if not handled diligently; and c) properly managing this condition is unbelievably time-consuming, which can take an emotional toll. Rob's parents were determined that type 1 diabetes was not going to be a burden for their boy. This was an obstacle, a hindrance to advancement that not only could be overcome, but would sculpt an intelligent and athletic boy with promise who could achieve anything in his life beyond his wildest dreams.

Imagine a world with no limits, no constraints, no boundaries. Today, many kids grow up with rigid walls in their education and at home, with pressure to conform and fit in. It seems that creativity belongs to the chosen few. Unfortunately, as a result, we're developing fewer Rob Campbells in the world, people who make an impact on a large scale and who do so for intrinsic reasons based on their values and belief system rather than for external recognition.

Rob got his first taste of this "no limits" philosophy after community members at his local church helped raise money for him to attend Camp Joslin for kids with type 1 diabetes. If you look back on the life of any high achiever, you'll undoubtedly find a time when they were given an opportunity. As Malcolm Gladwell relays in his book *Outliers*, it's not just the 10,000 hours of practice that makes someone a master, but key opportunities that came about to be able to put that practice into action and create memorable change. For Rob, his experience at Camp Joslin was his first opportunity and he credits his time there with sparking his interest in working in the diabetes world.

What started as a two-week camping experience in 1977 turned into a fuel for Rob as his eyes opened to the larger diabetes world. Rob met all kinds of kids from all over the world battling the same condition; he no longer felt so alone. He would go on to serve as a camp counselor and eventually as the director, where he would hire, train, educate and oversee the entire program. "It just inspired me to see what an impact a small team of dedicated people can have on so many lives. It was my first lesson in life. Apply your learnings and give it back." When Rob said that it stirred something inside me because he learned this at such an early time in his life. For most of us, this learning takes a lifetime.

As Rob recalls his time at Joslin, it is obvious that the experience stirred something inside of him to embrace change, own his circumstances, take action and be responsible. "People with diabetes just have to grow up a lot quicker. There's no way around it," Rob says. His parents could not have known at that time the force of Rob's personality beginning to take shape. It is Rob's passion for life fueled by his parent's encouragement mixed with athleticism and an engineering mind that spurred Rob on to seek out challenges, particularly when it came to exercising his physical gifts.

The meaning of life is to find your gift, the purpose of life is to give it away.

—Pablo Picasso

Cycling, rowing, running, skiing, in-line skating and track and field are just a few of the sports that gave Rob what he was seeking: individual challenge and transformation coupled with the understanding that great things can happen in teams. After intensive workouts at crew practice that tested his mind and body, he would run 400-meter sprints with his teammates to cool down. It occurred to him and others right away that while Rob had a variety of athletic gifts, he was also really, really fast.

IT NEVER HURTS TO ASK

Here's a guy who walked up to the coach of the Humboldt State University (in Northern California) track and field team, telling him that he'd like to run. The coach looked at him like he was crazy. But after inviting him to the track and seeing him run, the coach was convinced. Rob went on to run the 4x100, the 4x400, the 200 meter and the individual 400 meter at the Division 2 collegiate level. (Note to self and others—ask for what you want in life.) Despite his excellence on the track, running wasn't Rob's first passion. He recalls training with his rowing team as one of his fondest memories. Consistent with his "be prepared" philosophy, he would carry honey in that all too familiar plastic honey bear jar in case of low blood glucose. Imagine a bunch of guys in their physical prime, rowing at night so they can boost their endurance and team-building with a honey bear in the boat. "The guys would all laugh, but they all knew about my condition because they had to. One of the most important things you need to do as a type 1 is to let those around you know and educate them. You're not alone in this and it's part of who you are. It could save your life one day."

If all of these sports weren't enough, Rob enjoyed a taste of the extreme as well. It appears that pushing yourself to new heights isn't enough unless there's some adrenaline to go along with it! Rob and his friends would in-line skate down the 101 bypass near Klamath, Calif., for miles and at speeds over 40 mph. My guess is that this wasn't what Rob's parents had in mind with the whole "no limits" attitude!

There's no question in my mind, however, that all of these experiences fostered a deep conviction in Rob that he could achieve anything. Now, at 44, Rob still plays. He's an accomplished alpine skier. He still loves the outdoors, cyling, hiking, in-line skating, kayaking and running and is a self-admitted adrenaline junkie, just a more prudent one today. His pursuits athletically notwithstanding, it was truly Rob's intellect that pulled him to Humboldt to pursue a degree in engineering.

THE PRAGMATIC DREAMER

When Rob was approached to join the Insulet team, he was consulting for a non-invasive glucose monitoring system both as a study participant as well an educator on topics around diabetes management. That's what Rob calls "in between jobs."

What I really find so inspiring about Rob is that he is a dreamer, an innovator, an engineering marvel who is committed to personally finding ways to improve his own condition while at the same time always looking to make a huge difference for people with type 1 diabetes.

He's a dreamer, but also a pragmatist. He hopes for the best, yet knows the kind of work it takes to make hope a reality. He gets after it and has no shortage of confidence, but that's also tempered with humility and great kindness.

OPPORTUNITY COMES KNOCKING

Rob had diabetes for 24 years when his personal physician came calling with an introduction to two other individuals identified by Prism regarding the "Insulet project." He was a little wary. Rob told me that for four decades, there have been claims of cures and technological advances that had promised great things for people living with diabetes, but they were never delivered. "It gets frustrating after a while," he says. "I wanted to be very optimistic about the journey, but I knew how challenging it would be."

With that, Rob still couldn't resist. Here he was being asked to be a key member of a small team that would eventually develop the first programmable, wearable, integrated insulin pump in the history of diabetes. He was given a blank sheet of paper. The time was here and now: The dreamer with decades of personal and professional experience with diabetes, along with an engineering degree, finally had his opportunity to change his life and the lives of millions of people suffering from this chronic disease. Finally, Rob could apply his most impressive and unique skill set toward his greatest passion. We should all be so lucky to find that kind of energy and fuel every day, the energy derived from deeply held values and a clear sense of purpose; the feeling that what you do really matters and that you can influence great change and make a difference.

Please know that Rob is very quick to point out that like any great pursuit, particularly of this magnitude, you can't do it alone. Rob credits an incredible team of mechanical, electrical, software and manufacturing engineers and many others that brought this dream to a reality. Rob talks about his team members as if they are a unified crew team and they might as well be. "We knew before we even pursued what needed to be done, what kind of people we needed."

It's the nimble, no limits, everything is possible enthusiasm that drives Insulet. "We have dreamers, adrenaline junkies with no let up and no fear to take on the giants," Rob says. He repeatedly has to pause and fight back emotion while he talks about how much he appreciates and values all of those on his team who have continued to carry the baton and advance their cause. "When you have this kind of team and combine it with a visible goal, no matter how lofty, great things will happen," Rob says.

The market opportunity was clear. While John L. Brooks sought a better way for his son, he is also an incredibly smart businessman and knows an opportunity when he sees it. This one was just more personal. Only 10 percent to 15 percent of the market at that time was using insulin pumps. That was perplexing, and Rob and his team needed to better understand the barriers of the market.

"Pump technology hasn't really changed in over 30 years when you stand back and look at it," Rob said. There were also a lot of skeptics. "This was about overcoming and driving beyond what everyone knew as limitations in order to design and develop the next generation of diabetes management products."

Far too often people with type 1 diabetes don't have a voice, so that's where they started. "We spoke with patients, nurses, doctors, and tried to understand why so few patients were utilizing pump therapy," Rob says. "Market research tells you the barriers and benefits of what already exists, but it doesn't tell you what to do or how to innovate and what kinds of risks you should take. That's why we needed a team with a unique, distinctive personality that was connected to our mission. They also needed to do it with passion, speed and modesty."

Their research pointed to four key design parameters for their product: safety (reliability), ease of use, discreetness and affordability. Simple, clear, direct. From my experience, this is the formula for any great company. Rob has held many roles at Insulet and was initially responsible for creating the product specifications and defining the user interface on the device. They all needed to align with those four parameters and it challenged just about everything that was common in type 1 products available at the time.

MISSION: POSSIBLE!

To even think about an integrated system that you can wear without having to deal with multiple pieces to assemble yourself was considered impossible. The ease of use and discreet design parameters forced a clear strategy to innovation and provoked many kinds of out-of-the-box questions. If it was integrated and discreet how could you make it small? Since you were dealing with an advanced technology, how could you make it disposable and affordable to remove all the technical barriers? These and countless other questions were discussed, argued, negotiated, countered and ultimately agreed upon. Despite so many varying opinions on what could work, the mission was clear. "We all knew everyone had the best intentions. It was just how we got there that varied," Rob says. That is an extremely healthy outlook: letting everyone be heard, considering options, exploring new ways and valuing people's input to go beyond what anyone has set out to do. This is what most companies don't get. They often lose sight of the mission they've committed to when they run into challenges, arguments and crossroads. It, too often, becomes about them and not about the customer need. "We are hyper customer-focused. We're doing this to help people living with diabetes. That's always front and center and needs to be," Rob says.

WINNING THE RACE

Type 1 diabetes is a marathon. Rob showed me that it is best managed in a series of sprints. His energy and spirit are contagious and, as a parent of a young type 1 child, I'm grateful and thankful that Rob is so committed to others in the type 1 marathon. He reminds us all that we don't need to win the marathon every day, but we just need to finish the race. It's that mindset that provides people with more freedom, just what Rob and his team were looking to do.

Today, in over 12 countries and growing, more than 50,000 people with diabetes around the world wear the OmniPod and credit the innovative design with enabling them to live their lives with no limits, a fuel that catapults Rob and his team to respond in no letup fashion. It's amazing what a small team of motivated, smart and energetic people can accomplish with clear objectives driven by a consumer need. Necessity is indeed the mother of all invention. Insulet is the fastest growing insulin pump company of all time. Of course, Rob responds to that in his modest fashion: "There are so many people in the world just like me."

I can only smile as I think to myself, "Wow, if only that were true."

MORGAN PATTON

Athlete
Diagnosed in 1995 at age 7

Secretariat, one of the greatest racehorses of all time, wore blinders. For a racehorse or draft horse, blinders or winkers are used to literally blind them from distractions. Placed in a bridle, these blinders keep horses focused only on what is in front of them and prevent them from being spooked by a passing horse.

When Morgan Patton's stepfather, Bruce Hall, a metaphorical wordsmith, told her that she was like "a horse with blinders," he was clearly describing his daughter's inability to see the big picture, and her fierce stubbornness in doing things her own way. Knowing her passion for horses, he utilized the analogy to give her a keen understanding of this double-edged trait.

Morgan was 5 years old when her parents got divorced. When her mom, Debbie Hall, remarried two years later, Bruce would become her father figure and her male role model. It was his consistency that Morgan recalls as she speaks of him fondly. "He was always around and loved me for who I was," Morgan says. He cared a great deal about Morgan, and since he was not her actual father, he wanted to make his presence even stronger and give her memories that she could always look back on.

Bruce was her diabetes surrogate. His commitment to Morgan's development came from the perspective of a devoted father. "I want to be her dad," Bruce told Debbie. "I want to be in charge of diabetes." Morgan looks back with gratitude and deep appreciation. Whether it was an overnight blood sugar check or a motivating conversation, Bruce was always there. Sadly, he passed in 2009, but he left her with gifts that would last her a lifetime. His fatherly love and consistent parenting after her biological father left planted seeds within Morgan that would eventually sprout, but only when she would begin to find her true passion.

In addition to the family upheaval at such an early age and a strong desire to reconnect with her biological father, Morgan reluctantly was forced to move to a different state when her mother relocated them from Ohio to Florida to live with her aunt. Not only do I sympathize with Morgan here, but I can empathize as well. My parents got divorced when I was 8 years old. We lived in Syosset, Long Island, so although my dad was only 40 minutes west of us in New York City, at that age it felt like he lived in another state. Of course, I realize there is a big difference between a father who leaves you and a father who just moves away. Even with that, however, I can feel Morgan's longing—her need, really—to reconnect with her birth father. A father figure is not a father. At that age it can also create anger with the father figure because part of the child's experience is that this person is trying to replace someone who really can't be replaced. Even if the figure is not trying to replace their parent, that almost certainly is how the child feels. It's certainly how I felt with my stepfather. He was devoted, kind, fun and supportive. I loved him and still do, but at that young age, I not only wanted my father, I desperately wanted him to care. As Morgan and I discuss this shared experience, it becomes clear that the more loving the father figure, the more potential tension and anger it can create that the child is not experiencing that from their biological parent. There were many radical changes in her life—the move, her father leaving—and whether it was stress, coincidence or both, Morgan would soon begin to experience symptoms of diabetes.

As Morgan begins to speak about this time in her life and the events leading to her diagnosis, you can feel a wisdom and strength far beyond her 24 years. "I was so young, but there are certain things I can vividly remember," she says. "I was wetting the bed every night, which was really embarrassing because I had moved on from that stage. My mom thought it was just the stress of the move and my father leaving."

One day, Morgan fell asleep in class. That episode, combined with her raging thirst, prompted her mother to take her to a primary care physician. Diagnosis: type 1 diabetes. With a blood glucose level in the 500s, she spent three days at Tallahassee Memorial Hospital. Her pediatric endocrinologist, Dr. Larry Deeb, who remained her doctor until age 20, walked into her room and proceeded to give Morgan her first injection of insulin, right then and there. "He just stabbed me with a needle," Morgan said accusingly. Dr. Deeb responded, "This is how it's going to be."

FIERCELY INDEPENDENT, OVERCOMING FEAR

Just a few months later, at the age of 7, Morgan would be giving herself shots. With her independent and competitive spirit, Morgan didn't want to feel that she couldn't do something. One morning before school, Morgan summoned her courage and got into a knee tuck position. She was planning to give herself a practice shot. With her knee pressed into her upper arm to push her skin out, she quietly affirmed, "I can do this," and proceeded to slowly inject a needle into her upper arm. She was immediately delighted, not only at her own courage, but more important by the fact that it didn't hurt. In her excitement, she ran to her mom and began injecting herself multiple times so that she could see her independence and courage. Bruce's office was only a block away, so she ran to his office, got up on his drafting table chair and showed him, too. It was a memory and a moment in Morgan's life that she looks back on fondly. She found courage and it gave her confidence that she could overcome the physical fear of needles as well as the mental fear of handling her own condition. It was her first lesson in taming fear; to move past it, you must confront it. The fear tends to always be greater than the actual experience.

Morgan didn't think much about the diagnosis early on. It wasn't that she didn't accept her diabetes; after all, she was very young. She just didn't have much comprehension of what diabetes meant, nor did she have an opinion about it. I could imagine that this dynamic only added to her fierce independence and Morgan wanting her own voice. "It wasn't that my parents didn't tell me the consequences of what could happen with type 1 diabetes," she said. "It's just that the rules didn't apply to me at that time."

THE GROUNDWORK FOR CHANGE

Morgan is so far removed from that period in her life physically, emotionally and mentally; however she talks about it in such a candid and emotional way. "I had a lot of resentment at that time in my life as an early teen," Morgan said. Resentment toward her mom ("I believed she was not doing enough to reconnect me with my birth father.") as well as the diagnosis of a chronic disease at a young age. "It built up a lot of rebellion and anger and ended up causing me a lot of problems with my health in that I just wasn't taking care of myself," she added. "I was a punk and I dealt with it by not dealing with it." That misdirected independence would begin to manifest in more negative ways fueled by her feelings of inadequacy.

Not realizing that her mom was protecting her from her father for her best interest, Morgan became angry with her that she had no relationship with him. After her father left, she would get an occasional birthday card or present. They only spoke a few times in the subsequent years from childhood to early teens. "I always blamed my mom for that," Morgan says. By the time she was 14, Morgan was trying to overachieve to get attention from her biological father. She made a concerted two-year effort to reconnect, but she found it was not a two-way street. She realized that all she wanted was for Dad to be proud of her. I think in the end, that's most of what we want from our parents, the feeling that we're valued and seen. It's akin to being deprived of oxygen: When you don't get enough, it becomes your main preoccupation. When she graduated a semester early from high school and told her father that she got into Florida State, he responded with a flat and inauthentic, "That's great." Her efforts to connect and have a relationship with her own father were failing and she internalized it.

Coming from a broken family myself, I believe one of the hardest things about divorce or separation from a parent is that a child feels like it is all about them. Their story has them as the lead character playing the victim. As we all know, the younger we are, the more the world seems to revolve around us. Since that is the case, when a family breaks up or a parent leaves, a child often perceives that it is partly or entirely his or her fault. This perception became too much for Morgan and during that time in her life, the lack of oxygen from her father prevented the healthy seeds previously implanted by Bruce to grow. As an only child, Morgan didn't have to share or ask for anything. She realizes now how that can create a self-centered, narrowed worldview, seeing things in only how they affect you. That selfishness created a desperate and lonely feeling, an emptiness that she did not know how to fill.

Much of this void played out in Morgan's diabetes self-care. For example, Morgan thought that checking her blood sugar was annoying. She wasn't ashamed at all about having type 1; she recalls just being lazy. "I figured insulin was like a vitamin so it was OK if I skipped it," she said. "I did what I wanted to do because I had my own rules." It was Morgan's independent and competitive spirit that ultimately endangered her because she had no healthy outlook or outlet. At the age of 16 in 2005, Morgan had an A1C of 16.8, which equates to an average blood glucose of over 430. Staggering.

Shortly after, Morgan and her family realized the dire urgency to make sure she took her insulin on a regular basis. "I felt awful," Morgan said. "I don't think I realized what I was really doing to myself. Not taking insulin was no longer an option as a result of how I felt." With her deteriorating condition, Morgan and her mom agreed with the endocrinologist's suggestion that an insulin pump would be the necessary adjustment to ensure regular insulin delivery.

Once Morgan started using an insulin pump, she immediately lowered her A1C to 13. While that was a quick improvement, she also gained 15 pounds in the process. Despite the weight gain, she felt better. She also realized that some exercise was now necessary for both weight control and to counteract the sustained hyperglycemia, so she started riding her bike to school. She discovered her passion: Morgan fell in love with bike riding. It would make the next coincidental discovery in her life that much more meaningful and powerful as it set the stage for a dramatic come-from-behind victory, a victory that would be won with a decreased A1C and an increased self-esteem.

AS FATE WOULD HAVE IT

During Christmastime in 2005, Debbie Hall was at a local pub in Tallahassee. She was introduced coincidentally to Joanna Southerland, mother of Team Novo Nordisk (formerly Team Type 1) founder Phil Southerland (see page 1). When they discovered that they each had a child with type 1, there was a lot to talk about. When Debbie asked how Phil was doing, Joanna responded, "Actually, great." Debbie then said, "I have a 17-year-old who hates me and her diabetes." This proved to be a fateful day because after sharing personal stories, hardships and the ongoing challenges around managing blood sugar levels, Joanna encouraged Debbie to have Morgan spend two weeks with Phil and his friends at Team Novo Nordisk. She knew that her son's attitude, his outlook and his involvement with Team Novo Nordisk was sure to be an inspiration to Morgan. And it was.

When Morgan received an email from Phil suggesting he could use her help for the cycling event Race Across America in 2006, she leaped. "I remember seeing all these kind of super-hero, super-fit people and they were all checking themselves," she exclaimed. "What I learned very quickly was it was NOT cool to NOT check your blood sugar!" That was a pivotal moment for Morgan, mentally. She finally was able to link managing her diabetes to a higher purpose and taking responsibility for what mattered to her. What mattered to her was doing fun, intense and crazy things. "Racing bikes at 30 mph is crazy and fun," she says in an ecstatic tone.

We're all attracted to successful people, however we define success. The discovery that she loved biking was now reinforced with this important life discovery. "I'm attracted to successful people," she said. One of the key lessons for Morgan early on was that to be successful in racing as a person with type 1 diabetes, you had to be regularly checking your blood sugar.

~~~~~~

A Personal View: Checking Blood Sugar

Parents always talk about this issue in family camps or support groups. How many times should you check blood sugar? Can you check too much? How do you know if you're checking enough? What's clear from high performers is to check regularly and consistently. While you should always consult your doctor on this issue, we use a simple rule of thumb in our family. If you find yourself guessing at where a blood sugar may be, then it's best to just check. We don't check inside of two hours after insulin dosing unless there is some behavioral reason to do so.

~~~~~~

For Morgan, it became clear that she needed to check frequently based on the fact that the racers ride fast and they ride long. They also happen to check themselves frequently. "I realized that if I was checking myself more often I could ride longer and faster!" This may seem obvious, but took a great deal of self-awareness from someone who was very stubborn, an outright rebel with blinders on.

Morgan's relationship with Phil, her diabetes mentor, would only grow stronger. In 2007, Phil sent her a kit. A simple kit, really, but for a 19-year-old girl discovering herself, it would become a significant turning point in her life. "It was the coolest thing ever," Morgan says excitedly. There was a jersey, socks, a water bottle and other team tools. Morgan was now part of something bigger than herself, part of a team. Phil Southerland truly got it. He knew that for him to really manage his diabetes, he had to connect it to something—a hook—a way of linking self-care to greater purpose and performance. It wasn't just about Morgan now. She was part of a team. A team that typecast themselves as achievers, limitless and goal-oriented. Her old self typecast of rebellion and anger at her disease began to fade. She was about to live her life with passion.

A BORN COMPETITOR

The come-from-behind story led to one of her proudest years in 2012 with Team Novo Nordisk. She finished second at the Kelley Cup in Baltimore and had a sixth place finish at National Racing Calendar (now NCC, National Criterium Calendar) in Somerville, N.J. She also competed in Speedweek, a grueling seven races over nine days with hour-long races in Georgia every night from Athens to Sandy Springs. She finished an incredible 12th place, overall. As if it is not enough to manage your racing and your blood sugar for one day, Morgan stretched that to nine consecutive days. Unreal. She was now a core part of the professional women's team racing all over the country. "I was gone all the time," she says.

Despite the success, there were constant stressors and challenges. "Diabetes made it more challenging," she says. The travel, missing people at home, and the occasional quick food were all stressors. "It's emotionally draining and stress messes with your blood sugars," Morgan says. "There were DNF's (Did Not Finish) and times where you could just be so inconsistent. I would have a DNF one week and the next week I'd come in second place." On top of her trying to compete physically, emotionally and mentally, she had the added dimension of having to be totally dialed-in on her management during races for optimal physical performance. "If you're a bit off or one thing goes wrong, that could be the end of your day," she said.

In one race she recalls the downward cycle where things begin to spin out of control. As Morgan was pounding on her bike, the smooth and rapid acceleration of her motion was disjointed. Her head began to throb and she could feel the lactic acid building up in her trunk. She was pushing harder now, but going slower. The dehydration was rapid at this rate and then her pump malfunctioned. While she knew she was working harder and going slower, the negative thoughts were the only things speeding up for her. "I'm high, this is horrible," she thought. "Stupid pump!" "How did I let this happen to myself? I know better!" With that her race would quickly come to a DNF. While Morgan was growing as a person, she was still a teenager, and not so far removed from her rebellious and independent ferocity. Morgan admits that she still gets very annoyed and frustrated with herself in those moments. In this situation, she had let both herself and her team down (something she just can't take), exacerbating a cycle of negative self-talk and plunging her into a state of distress.

CATALYST FOR CHANGE

As a competitive racer—notwithstanding diabetes—she has learned how better to manage her attitude, limiting or preventing the fight-or-flight response to stress. That didn't come easily for Morgan and she's still growing as an individual and an athlete. She recalls those years of rebellion and self-sabotage in her previous typecast. "I was only hurting myself, and it's funny, now when I talk to kids who were just like me, I can look at them and say genuinely, `You're only hurting yourself.' "

We all intuitively know that we cannot make someone do anything. They need to come upon that for themselves. We can help facilitate that process and open doors for their own dramatic comebacks or raise the level of how they take care of themselves. Morgan affirms that she is a huge believer in this aspect of human behavior and loves to show, not tell. She's figured out that asking questions and letting people discover their own answers not only facilitates learning, but also fuels their spirit and gives them a catalyst for change. She also loves to give back in this way. Whenever she has a race, she will try and connect to all kinds of support networks—JDRF, support groups, children's summer camps, or the American Diabetes Association—to be able to speak to kids and adults. The day before a race in Cincinnati, she stopped to speak to a group of kids and adults with type 1. She shared stories and answered questions. She knew the best lesson would be the one where actions speak louder than words. The next day she went out and won her event with all of those people looking on, a sharp reminder to everyone: find what motivates you and you can achieve your dreams regardless of your condition.

This is a powerful lesson in parenting young children with type 1. As parents, we all have our tendencies and ways in which we want to manage *their* diabetes. As much as our heart goes out to them and we feel we know what is good for them, it is their condition, not ours. There has to be a sense of empowerment and ownership for them, more than just being told what to do or how much to check or what and when to eat and constantly being re-minded to be careful or remember your glucose tablets. As Morgan reminds me, "Diabetes is a constant stressor. It's always there and life is complicated by the fact that there is always this backdrop of a chronic condition around everything you do."

Many times our best intentions produce exactly what we're trying to defend against. We want our children to be prepared, be aware, check themselves and fortify themselves nutritionally. We want them to exercise, understand the different influences of certain foods on their blood sugar and we want them to get plenty of sleep so they can better metabolize insulin and regulate their weight. We may feel the only way to do this is to remind, coerce, incentivize, punish or do whatever it takes to fuel their adherence. The more we stress and the more we make type 1 the top urgent priority, the more we are adding to the constant stressor in their life. Paradoxically, the more you push them, the more likely they are to be non-adherent to their treatment plan. Kids sense desper-ation and it only pushes them away. As parents, we all know how true that is.

Here is where it gets challenging, though. Kids don't know what is necessarily good for them, so it's our job to make sure they take care of themselves. Of course, that's true, but many times how we're trying to get there is counterproductive.

What I learned from Morgan and from what I know about human behavior and engagement, people's core need emotionally is to feel valued, to feel adequate, that they belong. When we harp or push things on our children around a condition they know is not only stressful, but inherently makes them feel different, it is in direct violation to their feeling valued and their sense of adequacy.

A Personal View: Tapping Into What Moves You

The key that unlocked Morgan's rebellion and opened the door to acceptance simply lies in the fact that she was able to see a group of people feeling empowered, owning their condition and thriving with it. Most important, Morgan now belonged somewhere. She felt a connection to her deepest values around fun, competition, adventure and excitement, all shared by her type 1 brethren. It was not just a simple kit that Phil Southerland thought would be fun for Morgan. He intuitively knew that if you can tap into what moves you, then the rest can be easy. We tend to think of test strips, pumps and needles as tools. While they are the tools to use, the missing tool is what motivates a person to be pulled to those tools, not pushed. For Morgan, that racing kit was a more powerful tool than any diabetes management tool. That kit was the key that unlocked Morgan's resistance to taking care of her diabetes. Find out what that is for your loved one and they will show themselves the way. You'll smile in the background as they thrive.

We've seen it with Gavin. He's only 6, but he wants to do things his way. Gavin is really into Power Rangers. He asked Tara why none of the Power Rangers take insulin. As you can imagine, that was one of those unexpected questions in rearing a child with diabetes. We talked about it and our message to him now is that the Power Rangers cannot do what they want or show strength without insulin. With his shots we now have the opportunity to help him understand that every time insulin gets into his bloodstream he can also be a Power Ranger. When we push, we usually push away. When we present a framework and he's empowered to be flexible within that framework he pulls. Set the right environment, encourage their role in helping themselves, empower their spirit and connect it to what matters most to them and they will find a path to not just surviving, but thriving. We all want to be somebody. Whatever that is, it's what makes us unique. Morgan's advice on compliance is simple. "Provide the tools, education, camps and anything to introduce them to a variety of people." That's how you find their trigger, and it's different for everyone. When they find what triggers them, what excites them and their sense of purpose, taking care of themselves becomes automatic in their redefined journey.

We have a responsibility to help our kids become responsible for themselves. When we all feel ownership, we feel empowered. With empowerment comes freedom. Allow your loved ones to feel as free as possible in a world where they are jailed by a chronic condition.

COMING TO TERMS

Jimmy Patton has likely had many regrets in his life. He has pushed people away, either from self-loathing or feelings of great inadequacy. It's sad when I think about how some people truly can't get out of their own way and can't find a way to deal with problems or challenges in their life. Recently, Jimmy tried to kill himself. As Morgan's father lay in the hospital, Morgan had to face the fact that Dad had his own issues to deal with, but she didn't want to see anyone be hurt in this way. Jimmy Patton was still her father, despite everything. Even with all of the detachment, the feeling that she was never good enough and the longing for a deeper connection, Morgan could only think about his wellbeing. I would say this young woman matured.

She is thankful to her mother who kept her from Jimmy in those early years. Clearly, she knew something that could not be explained to a little girl whose father left her. Morgan is very well aware now that there are issues with her father beyond her comprehension. While that can only lead to speculation and the unknown, what Morgan knows for sure is that it was never about her. As much as she thought that her dad wanted nothing to do with her, it turns out that he didn't feel equipped to be a father at the level he needed to be for this special little girl.

In Morgan's Words

"You can only help yourself. No one else can make you feel good or happy."

THE BLINDERS COME OFF

Today, Morgan has come a long way. Not just in racing, but in her life development. It's hard for me to imagine how she must have been during those days of hyperglycemia and stubbornness. She speaks like a woman who is both confident and humble, not surprising coming from Team Novo Nordisk and a Phil Souther-land-influenced background. At this writing, Morgan had some incredibly exciting news to share. While she was about to pursue a degree in nursing to become a certified diabetes educator, Phil asked her to oversee the Women's Program for the race team. The recognition from them was clear—they didn't want her to go. With a new sponsor, bigger events, increased resources to recruitment and worldwide attention, Team Novo Nordisk needs Morgan Patton for her strength and her fire. Not only is she racing full time, but she's also a spokesperson to inspire people to get on their bikes. With the recognition from Phil and Team Novo Nordisk coupled with her maturity and her fierce independence yielding into a team player, Morgan had her best year ever racing in 2012.

When I ask her what she is most proud of recently, she responds, "last May." She finished in third place at the Tour of Somerville in front of her mentor and consistent supporter, Phil, and members from her team looked on. It was a big race for the team because their sponsor at the time, Sanofi, was located just a few miles from the race course. Morgan delivered. "It was a big day for me," she says with a smile of great internal satisfaction that I can feel come through the phone.

Having also accepted the leadership position for the women's cycling team, she says it's a place for women with diabetes to be the best you can be. "If they need bigger shoes to fill we give it to them. We want our women to be the best athletes they can be, to mentor them on all of the issues surrounding their management and to let them discover for themselves what can be personally transformational."

She now gets to race and focus on her life mission: inspire others and give back. For Morgan Patton, it's been a long journey. She has not looked back from those early days. The blinders are off and it is eyes wide open.

JEFF HITCHCOCK

Founder, Children With Diabetes
One child diagnosed—Marissa in 1989 at age 2

"The person with diabetes who knows the most lives
the longest."

—Dr. Elliott Joslin

A MODERN RELIC

LOG ONTO WWW.CHILDRENWITHDIABETES.COM AND YOU SHIFT
back in time to the early years of the Internet.

Its long menu items, static display ads, scrolling pages and
text give it a Web 1.0 feel. And yet, the site is one of the largest
in the world dedicated to diabetes. It hosts over 35,000 pages,
counts more than 20,000 visitors per day and delivers millions of
pages of information per month, making it one of the most trusted and comprehensive portals for type 1 diabetes ever created. It's
ranked among the best medical websites in the word. You would
be challenged to find another site like it, especially one that has
become so radically successful. "You'll see mainly what science
supports," says Jeff Hitchcock, its founder and technologist. "The

site is designed to provide good information and help people connect. It's efficient."

MONDAY MORNING DIAGNOSIS

This story, like many others, begins with love as its inspiration, and a clear mission that fueled its longevity and continued success. Jeff and Brenda Hitchcock were married in 1984 after they met in Kinshasha, Zaire. They had both been working for the federal government in different departments and their trips overlapped, a fateful coincidence. Their first child, Marissa, was born in 1987. It would not be very long before they recognized that something was wrong with her. Marissa's thirst was unquenchable and her diapers were soaked through nightly.

Their visit to the pediatrician resulted in a yeast infection diagnosis, incredibly rare for a 2-year-old girl, and what should have been a sure sign of type 1 diabetes. The pediatrician missed the bigger problem and diagnosed a symptom, not the root cause. As Marissa's symptoms continued, Jeff and Brenda knew they had to go back to the doctor. On a Friday afternoon, they took her in and the pediatrician wanted a urine sample. As most anyone who cares for a type 1 baby or toddler knows, urine comes when it comes, certainly not by demand. So, the couple waited a long time with a plastic bag attached to Marissa to catch her sample. By the time she had to urinate, the office was closing, so the doctor took the sample for evaluation over the weekend. With Brenda home, Jeff had to fly to California that weekend for business. The grim news came in Monday morning. Marissa Hitchcock, at the age of 2, was diagnosed with type 1 diabetes, 10 days after their first visit to the pediatrician.

Jeff immediately flew home and joined his wife and daughter at Children's National Hospital in Washington, D.C. Despite the earlier missed diagnosis, she was not in diabetic ketoacidosis (DKA), a potentially life threatening complication that occurs when cells in the body are unable to get the glucose they need for energy. DKA results from too little insulin, and in response the body switches over to breaking down fat and muscle for energy, which causes the complications. Until insulin therapy started in the 1920's, it was universally fatal. In fact, Jeff shares only positive memories of their experience at the hospital. "They had a playroom that Marissa really enjoyed and she shared a room with another girl who was in for treatment of cystic fibrosis. That gave us immediate perspective."

That was certainly helped by the fact that their endocrinologist, Dr. Allen Glasgow, was incredibly positive. "Everything is going to be OK," he said. "Marissa will be fine." Encouraged and emboldened by their doctor, the Hitchcocks were able to focus on their daughter and not worry about all the unknowns and what was in front of them. After all, they knew it would all be OK. "We were extraordinarily lucky to get the medical team we did," Jeff says. "We won the lottery of a great team at diagnosis and that has had a major long-term impact."

A Personal View: First Impressions

As Jeff describes Marissa's diagnosis experience, I feel a bit of uneasiness thinking about our own. While certainly not negative, I realize now that it could have been much more positive. Why should we settle for care that feels like we just happen to be the most recent one in the door to be impacted by a growing epidemic? Shouldn't it be more individualized and personal? Do many medical professionals have *just another day* syndrome? Our doctor and hospital nurse were nice and attentive. They did, however, have an opportunity to completely shape how we would experience and think about diabetes going forward, and that was a lost opportunity for us. What was lost was the opportunity to approach diabetes care from a proactive stance, a feeling of hope. Upon diagnosis, our experience and that of many others we've discussed this with was fear and loss. Diabetes is a disease and as such, we feared having to take care of a sick child. I don't expect that to be completely eliminated. But I realize now that I was looking for something to hang onto, even a small grip for clammy hands; something I could hold along with my fear that my child will learn and overcome a great challenge, that he is not sick, and that with our support there will be nothing different in what he can achieve versus anyone else, or how long he can live a healthy and meaningful life. I hope that all endocrinologists, nurses and faculty members can serve up this reminder for themselves every day: What you do is vitally important and impacts lives. Make sure you impact in the most positive and lasting way possible.

In addition to Dr. Glasgow, Jeff credits Joe Ward, R.N., and Jill Benchill, Ph.D, CDE, a clinical psychologist, for their encouragement and positive outlook. Jill now serves as senior faculty for Children With Diabetes, so the relationship and impact from their positive experience around diagnosis and treatment has endured. We all deserve an opportunity for that at a particularly vulnerable time in our lives.

AN IDEA TAKES SHAPE

A software manager at the time of Marissa's diagnosis, Jeff gravitated to the Internet in search of more help and education on diabetes. He found a diabetes discussion area on CompuServe, one of the very first dial-up web browsers. While not robust, Jeff recalls that it was somewhat helpful early on.

What he found, though, was troubling. The site had a forum where negativity and fear were part of the fabric of many conversations. It was a valuable lesson for Jeff. Your overall positivity, how you treat others and how you manage diabetes is key to long-term health and happiness, and it would shape his view of how to provide diabetes education in the exact opposite fashion. It was clear that there should and could be a better way to learn about diabetes in a non-threatening way on the Internet, particularly for people who were new to this diagnosis. He also knew that the ability to share information and connect with others would be incredibly valuable, albeit not easy.

While Jeff had been thinking about utilizing the web as a great platform to start his own diabetes community, he was working full time and the web was just a fledgling new medium. Brenda had also left the workforce after their second daughter, Kathryn, was born in July, 1990. Not the best of combinations to bet your family's future finances on, most especially given the care Marissa needed along with the barriers of entry to the Internet.

Trying to build a website in the early 1990s was a bit different than today. The barriers to entry for an online business have virtually been eradicated with the advent of technology, design and hosting firms that are ever present now. What can be done in minutes today was a major challenge in 1994. There were essentially no vendors to support Jeff's needs. He had to set up a computer network, learn the Domain Name System for connecting computers to the Internet, pay for high-performance T1 servers and increase electrical capacity. He needed an improved HVAC system to cool the added and expensive equipment. Even with that backbone, it did nothing to help with all of the installation and configuration of software, web servers and the writing of delivery code, which at that time he was doing all by himself in Perl, a scripting language for many online applications. Everything had to be created, designed and installed, a huge financial commitment and far from any promise that the Internet would become what it is today. That takes more than just summoning up courage. Sometimes we need the impetus of not really having a choice to take necessary risks that can help us grow and reach new heights.

BEST LAID PLANS

Jeff had an opportunity to pursue his dreams when he was laid off after a one-year stint with a defense contractor in 1994. He turned his complete attention to developing his diabetes website, now only with the urgency of someone without an income who has to provide for his family. Inspired by Marissa, Jeff set out to create a platform where people could learn information supported by science and help connect families with diabetes.

So, Jeff set out to improve his knowledge to give him the best chance to succeed. He learned as much as he could about the Internet and building websites. He is self-taught in developing web pages and was likely one of the early adopters to have a T1 modem, typically a device reserved for businesses with large bandwidth needs, installed right into his home. At the time, it was like ordering a plane to park in your driveway.

Working tirelessly and burning through cash, Jeff knew he could not sustain this dream for very long with no income and a dwindling 401(k). The pressure of launching a startup in the unchartered waters of the Internet proved to be stormy and unpredictable. Waves of uncertainty and doubt occasionally washed over him, but he remained steadfast in his dream and passion, and most powerful of all, he was inspired and determined because this was about his little girl. Jeff's strong sense of purpose and unique skill set kept the idea of Children With Diabetes alive while Jeff set out to find supplemental income to make it through another day.

In the summer of 1995, Jeff landed a contract to build and host the Juvenile Diabetes Foundation's website, what we know today as JDRF. Jeff poured his energy and resources into making the partnership work, yet by February of 1996, it became clear to him that it was going nowhere. By now, his 401(k) had been spent, and family time was stressed due to the energy and resources he needed to devote to building his website. He had no choice. Jeff had to find a job and generate an income.

A job offer came from LexisNexis just in time. "It completely saved the day," Jeff says. Finally, there was money coming in and Jeff was able to continue building the site.

CHILDREN WITH DIABETES IS BORN

While Jeff pressed on, learning more about coding, developing web pages, finding hosting solutions and writing software programs,

CWD emerged to life. In June of 1995, Children With Diabetes launched with the clear goals of helping Marissa Hitchcock meet other kids who had diabetes and sharing the experiences of her parents, Jeff and Brenda.

In its first months, CWD was a homegrown Mom and Pop website. CWD consisted of Marissa's story, information and advice from Jeff and Brenda, listings of local ADA and JDRF chapters, reviews of books and products, some diabetes information, and links to other diabetes websites. The site contained roughly 100 pages. It was likely due to the homegrown appeal and the void in the market that this small start-up website, created after years of persistence and dedication, would result in families from all over the world finding their way to it.

It was also Jeff's realization that, in a dial-up era, he would have to keep graphics to a minimum. Even to this day, recognizing that not all countries possess broadband, he has stayed true and consistent with ensuring that accessing CWD remains as open and easy as possible. While many informational websites go through redesigns yearly, CWD has had essentially one redesign only two years after launch to be cleaner and to reveal a new logo. The interior pages have not changed since then and it has organically achieved a state of differentiation and authenticity that welcomes new visitors and stays true to its mission: share and connect.

As this was one of the only sites of its kind to offer families in need a trusted resource, it was not long before Jeff would get emails about medical questions. As a result, one of the most important and sustaining sections of the site was born. "Ask the Diabetes Team," comprised of medical doctors and certified diabetes educators, has become one of the most trusted and utilized areas on CWD and today is a unique and unrivaled medical resource. In its first 18 months, it answered more than 30,000 questions, more than 50% of them online.

CWD MEET THE INTERNET, INTERNET MEET CWD

The dawn of the Internet era and open access to free information was intersecting with a growing epidemic in diabetes cases. Jeff Hitchcock would find himself right at the center of this intersection in an unknown land, a huge responsibility that despite its clear opportunity came with no roadmap. What he did know was that running a website was extremely expensive, yet he wanted to maintain his goal of free and easy access. He decided to go to his user base and see if a pledge drive would work to avoid an advertising model that was beginning to be popularized on many websites in the dawn of this new era. It turned out to be unsuccessful, so he brought up the advertising prospect with his users. They said that it would not influence their usage of CWD and, given the increased costs of computer hardware and a growing Internet connection, CWD became advertiser-supported in 1998.

In the modern Facebook era where privacy mostly goes unprotected, Jeff Hitchcock has maintained integrity and security for his users. CWD's platform is built to maintain openness and a safe place where people can connect, share and help others learn about managing diabetes. Maintaining free and anonymous access to content was and continues to be a core tenet of the site, ensured by a privately built advertising server in which ads are not tracked. It's just another example of how unique and different this website is set apart from how the Internet has evolved today. In a world where personal information is sold and tracked all over the web, CWD is truly built for its user base and their interests.

CWD TAKES A SHOT

With a secure base and advertising revenue coming in, Jeff decided to really go for it and build out his website with the focus of becoming a major resource and moving beyond the passion project stage. He also recognized that this was requiring every ounce of his energy as a part-time, after-work venture. Since he was working after hours and on weekends, Jeff knew that if he was to keep the site going it would require a full-time effort. Even with that, he would need help.

By late 1999, Jeff attended a family diabetes retreat in Southern California. It was there that, after a discussion with close advisors, he formed a new company to include many more features and services and to morph into a fully comprehensive diabetes resource for the growing need among newly diagnosed families.

You have to remember that this was also right in the middle of the frenetic and rapidly growing investment into unproven websites with no earnings, just spectators excited about the prospects. This has come to be known as the "dot com bubble." In the middle of all this mayhem was a particularly attractive category: health care sites.

Once again, Jeff Hitchcock would find himself with an opportunity of a lifetime. His skill and talent notwithstanding, timing is the critical element to truly leverage opportunity and achieve greatness. It seemed as though it was all working for him. With the coupling of investment in the Internet and a growing user base, Jeff launched www.Diabetes123.com in April of 2000 to sustain the earlier framework he had built and the promise to significantly expand its offering and be of real value to his audience. As with any great achievement, it does not come easily. At the same time that Jeff was poised to really sustain and grow his website, he was confronted with the burst of the dot com bubble, yet another obstacle in his path to sustaining Marissa's inspiration. Very quickly, the focus of his business and his website shifted to surviving rather than growing.

While Jeff previously had managed to overcome an array of obstacles to get him to this point, the time would come where some outside help would not only buffer his company from the pressure on Internet sites, but would also set the stage for CWD's biggest differentiator in the marketplace: reaching beyond the impersonal digital walls of the web to forge touch points and personal experiences with his users. Little did he know that this outside help would actually be coming from someone so impacted by his creation. What may not be surprising is the fact that a young child's diagnosis would be the same source of inspiration and provide the fertile ground in which their relationship would grow and prosper.

BEYOND DIGITAL

In 1998, when Laura Billetdeaux was leaving the hospital after her son Sam was diagnosed at the age of 8, her world was spinning from feeling overwhelmed, concerned and afraid. After she got Sam to bed and had a moment to breathe, she took out the business card her diabetes educator had given her. On that card was a single resource to support families entering into this new and uncertain world of diabetes care: Children With Diabetes.

"You need to hear it's going to be OK," says Laura. "The rest you can learn. You're completely in survival mode at the point of diagnosis."

At 7 p.m., with a quiet home, her son sleeping into his first night of the rest of his changed life, Laura knew that things would never be the same. As she sat in front of the computer reaching out to the digital world for support and guidance, the tears started to flow. Laura found an area on www.childrenwithdiabetes.com at that time called "Friends." She posted about the diagnosis that evening of her precious little boy who had lost a piece of childhood innocence. She added, "I am so scared." Within a few minutes, responses came in. Inside of 30 minutes there were dozens of responses. Support came in from around the world to lift and hold her in that fragile time. She sat there as the tears washed over her. Laura knew things would be OK.

A speech pathologist for 20 years when Sam was diagnosed, Laura began having a hard time concentrating on clients and her business. With her heart and brain in diabetes, she realized that she was not doing her family or her clients any good. With her husband working, she decided to leave her job, not knowing exactly what she would do. A vacation with some of these families she was corresponding with on CWD seemed to be the right next move. She sent a note to other parents on the CWD email community list and what began as a simple email to a small group of users that read something like "Anyone want to meet in Orlando for a vacation?" became more than 100 families, 550 people altogether, getting together for several days of fun, relationship building and shared community. The response was overwhelming and Laura decided to approach Jeff for CWD to sponsor the event. It was clear there was interest from users of the site and this would be a great way for families to extend their bond outside the digital arena and really help CWD come to life. Jeff was focused on CWD being a web-based entity. "This is really not what one might expect from a web-based startup, particularly at that time," Jeff says.

He did agree to let Laura try to find a sponsor. He felt that if she was able to get a sponsor, they would be able to call it a CWD event. With a few contacts from Jeff, Laura set out to pursue the opportunity. With her heart and mind aligned around her sense of purpose, Laura had to learn a new skill. "I hate asking people for money," she says. "I was so nervous and even hung up the phone a few times." Her nerves, at first limiting, became the fuel for tenacity. (I'm reminded of a saying that I fall back on when I find myself justifying not doing things that can stretch me as a person. Pat Croce, former owner of the Philadelphia 76ers and health care entrepreneur says, "Always, always do what you're afraid to do.") After a fifth call to Steve Bubrick at TheraSense, now Abbott Diabetes Care, Laura knew his voicemail by heart. She expressed that this would be her last call, but she felt the opportunity would be a unique one and provide TheraSense a way to connect with a very targeted and receptive audience. Thirty minutes later she received a return call. "How's $10,000?" Bubrick asked. This first sponsorship paid for receptions and gatherings that provided a sense of family and community and were the catalyst for a new way to help families and CWD carry forward their mission. "Conferences completely differentiate us," Jeff says.

"FRIENDS FOR LIFE"

Jeff's technical experience is matched by a shrewd business acumen that has catapulted CWD into a welcome, albeit lonely, arena of trusted websites. He and Laura knew that bringing people together in annual conferences would not only create a cycle of growing users from word of mouth, but would be the touch point that would put a face on his website. He fully credits Laura for creating this opportunity for families from all over the world to come together, especially since he really just viewed CWD as a web-based support mechanism. Over the next four years, the conferences would broaden CWD's reach to the extent that there are now four conferences every year: the annual Friends for Life in July, two smaller regional conferences in the spring and fall and one vacation in the late winter or early spring. The conferences are much more than the word "conferences" can possibly reveal. They are powerfully moving experiences for participants that yield moments of great inspiration and connections for a lifetime. It's not surprising that the conferences are called Friends for Life. One attendee, Cindy Webb, wrote on the site: "The best thing that happened to our family was becoming involved with CWD."

In hearing from participants, it is clear that the experience goes beyond disseminating diabetes information, although there is plenty of that. What really shines through in these conferences is the sense of community, resilience and giving back. "The taught become the teachers," said Diabetes Dad, Tom Karlya (page 20) The courage of children is an amazing force that can humble any adult. I am reminded of Kelli Kuehne's (page 53) comment about her diagnosis being harder for her parents than it was for her. This inner strength that type 1 reveals is like a leaf revealing its true colors in the fall. Type 1 diabetes has a way of helping shy kids become leaders, lonely kids find like-minded groups and quiet kids shout at the top of their lungs. Laura reminds me that this resilience starts with the parents and the children model and reflect it back. This is such a great understanding and a powerful insight to what shapes children with diabetes. It's not just the adversity that builds the inner strength. It's the strength of the parents that builds the inner resiliency of the child. CWD is a multiplier of that effect.

Thanks to CWD and this conference, kids have the opportunity to show who they are, what they can be, but most of all, what they stand for; that with setbacks you can become stronger and there is nothing you can't achieve. Today, the conferences bring in thousands of people from around the world and its impact is immeasurable. This forum gives kids and adults alike the courage, resilience and sense of purpose that will fuel all of their life experiences and it all can be found at a conference that started with that one simple question, "Hey, does anyone want to meet in Orlando for a vacation?"

WORLDWIDE REACH

Even Jeff looks back in awe at what his part-time, self-built website has become. His focus on content and resources that can really make a difference for diabetes families is truly what sets this site apart. While many stories take a "we've arrived" turn after finding success or reaching a milestone, what I find truly incredible about CWD is how it has maintained its humble beginnings. Everything in the site from the beginning is still there today including the daily kids' stories about diagnosis that have not moved from the front and center of the home page, the most valuable piece of real estate for advertisers. Additionally, the "current poll" that engages the interactivity of the user and the "Family Support Network," which helps newly diagnosed families find the personal support they are anxiously seeking, have been mainstays and have provided the backbone of CWD since 1995.

When you factor in that not much has changed on the design side, CWD is a place you can trust because familiarity and consistency build that trust. It is plain that this website, which was built by a family's own personal experience on the back of a home Internet connection, continues to strike a chord with newly diagnosed families. Why? Because they've been there and they knew what they were looking for, what questions they had and what kinds of support they wanted. CWD is exactly what Jeff and Brenda wanted and needed after Marissa's diagnosis and what was so difficult to find. With Marissa as its inspiration, CWD now offers that for thousands of families around the world. For Jeff and his family there can be no greater reward. Consistency is a measure that is difficult to achieve in our world of fast moving business and new ideas trying to find traction in an easily distracted culture. The need to feel that if you're not growing you're dying is more present today within companies than at any point in our history. That this Mom and Pop website went beyond its capability to change lives is a case study in the making. How do you stay true to yourself and your mission while growing so that you remain who and what you are in the process? Look no further than CWD, a website inspired by a diabetes diagnosis that has spawned a community of inspiration and a clear mission: make a difference in diabetes. Log on and join the movement.

In Jeff's Words

"Our mission is to teach and support. We continue to make a difference."

LITTLE GIRL GROWN UP

Jeff will never forget the end of a chapter in his life that forged a new beginning. Before Marissa was diagnosed, Jeff and Brenda were going about their lives like all of us before the unforgettable day; working, enjoying family, planning and staying active with a variety of interests. The diagnosis was a shock. As I hear the Hitchcock story, I'm moved at how this supposed setback became the seed for a rich and nutritious source of family connection and support, built on the backbone of something meaningful. Coming to a loved one's aid in a way that any individual can influence is a powerful motivator and a reminder that we all need to live lives with purpose and to lift one another.

When Marissa was still just a little girl, she asked Dad, "Why would this happen to me?" He responded in a calm and encouraging manner. "Sometimes people that are stronger get things. You wouldn't have gotten this if you couldn't handle it." Marissa is clear and grateful about where her diabetes management comes from. "My family has always been there for me. Even when they weren't there, I was reminded of their love and encouragement." On her first sleepover at her best friend's house, which was allowed only after she was allowed sleepovers at other type 1 homes, her friend's father made sure she ate cheese following juice to sustain her blood sugar. "It was like my parents were there," she laughs. "I've been given control of my diabetes from an early age and I know that was not easy for my parents to let go, but is a big reason that I don't experience much negativity about my diabetes." That said, she recalled an incident where she was leaving the house and her pump cord got caught on a drawer, ripping her pump site out. "That really annoyed me, " Marissa said. She quickly realized that it wasn't that big a deal and got on with it. For a young woman, that demonstrates resilience and persistence, two key components of managing and living with type 1 diabetes.

At 26 now, Marissa is married and is a nurse at West Chester Hospital in Cincinnati, where she met her husband, who is also a nurse. She has a bright future ahead of her. She is expecting her first child, Jeff and Brenda's first grandchild. Marissa is excited to follow in the "giving back" footsteps and continues to marvel at her dad's creation and impact in the diabetes world. "It's so incredible, I'm so proud," she says. "CWD has helped me meet so many other kids with diabetes from all over the world, which has also helped me learn and grow outside of just the diabetes lens. One of my closest friends, Martin, lives in Glasgow, Scotland." It's just amazing how Jeff has opened these doors for like-minded people in need of support and connection. Marissa quickly reminds me that what so inspires her as being Dad's inspiration for CWD is that what she has experienced growing up—support and resources to benefit her—has impacted millions just like her.

"I really believe my dad's greatest contribution is that people feel at home at our events," she says. When you factor in the support, the latest research and education, the tools and access to thought leaders and doctors, what most grabs Marissa's enthusiasm is the support and acceptance that CWD provides. At its core, the digital platform and event company is housed under a mission of self-advocacy. Everything rolls up into that.

LIKE FATHER, LIKE DAUGHTER

What's fascinating to note is that while Marissa was a source of inspiration for her father in creating CWD, he has become a source of inspiration for her. Inspiring people has a reverberating and exponential effect. For the Hitchcocks, that means that the world benefits because Marissa is dedicated to giving back. She affirms that CWD has played a huge role in why she wants to give back. "I see every day what a difference my dad makes. I have such a loving family and for them to help, guide and support me drives me. I owe the world to my family. I'm doing what I'm doing because of them." She's tasted how good giving back feels for the donor and recipient and she's doubling down. In addition to nursing, she's never far from planning programs for teens for CWD events. Now, she also gets to do that with one of her mentors early on as she was coming up, Natalie Bellini. Natalie is a Certified Diabetes Educator (CDE) with type 1 who has been an educator and friend to her for the past 10 years.

It's hard to imagine life for Jeff and Marissa being any different at this point. Would Marissa prefer not to have type 1 diabetes? Of course. That still doesn't change the fact that her life is full of purpose and passion as a result of her condition. As a result, she is a world contributor just like her dad.

Laura remembers a poignant moment at one of the conferences when father and daughter sat together on the stage. The music playing was by popular country singer George Canyon, who, like Marissa, is also type 1. They held each other while Canyon's "Madi's Song (The Man She Thinks I Am)" played.

I'm just an ordinary guy
I can't stop bullets, and I can't fly
But I can be the one who dries her eyes when she cries
I may never be the man she thinks I am, but I'm gonna be
the best dad that I can.

DEREK ROWLEY

Business Analyst
Diagnosed in 2003 at age 13

"I THINK I HAVE DIABETES," DEREK ROWLEY TOLD HIS MOTHER after peeing on one of his brother's Ketostix.

"Derek, what made you check your urine?" asked his mother, Dr. Avril Beckford, who is our pediatrician in the Atlanta area.

He responded in a matter-of-fact tone: "Mom, I've been doing it for two years."

At the age of 13, Derek confronted what he had feared for eight years since his brother Justin was diagnosed. So here it is, he thought, and with that, the fear of getting diabetes was quelled. Now, like his older brother, he would have to deal with it.

Derek's father is also a doctor. Growing up with two parents as doctors can have its drawbacks. For one: "It seems that kids of doctors get sicker for some reason," Derek says. "On top of that they think there is never anything wrong with you." That is clearly not a good combination. What's clear about Derek's doctor-parent combo is what they have produced: A passionate, incisive, kind and wildly intelligent young man, who, at 24, beams with promise and optimism about what life can bring to those who go after it. If Derek was a stock, you would want in now and never stop buying. He's a will-be world changer and to speak with him before he breaks out is like having insider information on something really special.

THE SIBLING EFFECT

Derek was only 5 years old when Justin, then 7, was diagnosed with type 1 diabetes. As most young people coming out of college can relate to, having an education or awareness of something doesn't quite make up for the experience most employers are looking for. The same is true for Derek's exposure to diabetes at such a young age. Derek heard and saw his family manage diabetes. He watched his brother have blood sugars checked and insulin injected. He heard the conversations about carb counting, negotiations on insulin amounts and general discussions about diabetes. He was aware with no direct experience, because he was someone without diabetes in a diabetes household.

For Derek, that created a baseline anxiety, a fear of developing diabetes that hovered in the background of his life on a regular basis. It was not consuming or overwhelming, just a level of concern and anxiety that was ever-present. Fortunately, Derek lived in a very empowering and proactive environment. He never felt neglected for not having diabetes and he pursued all of his interests with great vigor. "In so many ways, he's become the man of the child he was," Avril says. "I'm just so proud of that."

~~~~~~

A Personal View: Staying True

One of Avril's earliest memories of Derek is from a teacher in preschool sharing with her that on the first day, when so many kids were upset about missing their parents, Derek was a source of support, comforting kids with friendliness and warmth. "I'm here, friend," he told his little classmates, "let me help you." Among all his great qualities, it's his huge sense of empathy, so innate, that stood out to his parents.

"From the age of 2, he just got it," Avril says. Derek always cared about others in a genuine way. His affection for others has been as consistent as any other quality. Even when very young, Derek would pat his loved ones twice on the back during a hug, a decidedly mature gesture. Evidently, it is innate for him, as he still does it to this day, giving his mom a constant feeling of the nostalgic love from her son.

His persistence, even pre-diabetes, was a mark of his character. "Whatever hurdle he's had, he jumps higher," says Avril, and "whatever gifts he's been given, he's maximized." Derek is a young man who knows who he is. Grounded in those values, he's poised to live a life of meaning and passion. Of course, he can do so many things given his talent and knowledge, yet with that he knows who he is and doesn't veer. "Despite his success, he's incredibly humble with his priorities and balance intact," his mother says. Staying true to ourselves is one of the most challenging aspects of our lives. There is a wonderful quote from Ralph Waldo Emerson that captures this: "To be yourself in a world that is constantly trying to make you something else is the greatest accomplishment."

GETTING SMARTER

In 1999, when Derek was 9, it became clear to him that the eventuality of diabetes was a distinct possibility. He participated in a study at the University of Florida in which children who had siblings with diabetes were having their blood drawn for research. These were a bunch of kids who had to see their brothers and sisters deal with this chronic disease daily, and the implication was that they may very well get it, too. Even if it was just research, the message to kids was clear—we're checking you because you're more likely than other kids to develop type 1 diabetes.

Derek's parents felt strongly that if there were studies available that could possibly yield preventive measures for him or could help the medical community with advances to a cure, it would be the responsible and prudent thing to participate in them. "Today, I tell parents to do what they are comfortable with," Avril says. Kids are smart and for Derek, a keenly aware boy, he knew exactly what he was being tested for, adding to his anxiety around the possibility of developing type 1 diabetes.

~~~~~~

A Personal View: The TrialNet Study

After Gavin was diagnosed, I took Jake to the TrialNet study for two reasons: to help researchers understand more about type 1 diabetes (there seem to be more questions than answers about how it's contracted), and to provide a certainty, if only for a year, that Jake would not get diabetes. Tara had mixed feelings about participating in this study. If Jake had no antibodies that would be nice to know; however, she didn't want to live her life with this baseline anxiety if he did have the antibodies. From what I've learned, parental baseline anxiety is there anyway. I wanted to rule it out or know that it was a possibility. Each time he comes up negative, we can feel that anxiety fade away, a one-year reprieve of not worrying about him developing type 1.

At the TrialNet office, Jake and Gavin were playing in the outside kids' waiting room. I watched them run and laugh, two brothers just hanging out and creating fun. I looked at all the siblings, one with diabetes, one without, interact with each other and play together as one. One dealt with a chronic condition, the other likely wondered whether he or she will get it. In that moment I realized, just like with Derek, there are also challenges for being the sibling without diabetes. Not only do you have the baseline anxiety of getting diabetes, but you have to watch your sibling deal with the constant care. You sympathize with their plight as you deal with potentially sharing their plight.

As parents, I'm not sure we can ever fully appreciate or empathize with the child who doesn't have diabetes. What I do know from Jake is that it's a lonely place at times and no psychologist can fill that void, but they can help.

The thought process goes something like this: *The fact is* my sibling has diabetes. *The story becomes* the proverbial rock and a hard place. *My sister has a chronic disease. I want them to find a cure for this. I hate to see what she has to put up with. I'm lucky that I don't have to deal with that, but there is a chance of getting it and sometimes I feel guilty for not having it. She definitely gets more attention than me because of her constant care so I don't feel as needed or appreciated, but is that worse than just having diabetes?* That's a lot for anyone to process and struggle with, let alone a kid.

Derek never felt neglected because of his brother's diabetes, and he certainly didn't want to get it. That would all change in June of 2003. His family had been at the beach all day and Derek recalls just feeling lethargic. "Something was off, I just didn't feel right." Immediately, he knew what it could be, so he pulled a urine-testing stick from Justin's supply drawer, peed on it, and became a self-diagnosed person with type 1 diabetes at the age of 13. His parents, Avril and Lawrence, took him to the Children's Hospital of Atlanta, a highly respected and nationally recognized children's hospital, where they confirmed Derek's finding.

From the moment of Derek's diagnosis, his parents were committed to helping support Derek with an alternative story, a path to another type of person that would be more empowering and present greater life options with no limits.

TO GO OR NOT TO GO

What came next was the beginning of an attitude and approach to diabetes that could benefit anyone.

While type 1 diabetes never seems to come at a good time, it came at a particularly bad time in Derek's life. Derek was in the final stages of preparing for a People to People trip that he was chosen for to go to Australia. Not only that, as any pre-teen with diabetes can attest, type 1 diabetes can wreak havoc on your blood sugar. According to Derek and others, the science of diabetes isn't exact during the teen years. Carbohydrate counting, ratios, insulin sensitivity factors and all the calculations we use to manage blood sugar become at best inconsistent. "Managing diabetes while hormones are secreting is a nightmare," Derek says.

Despite concern from his parents, in cooperation with their doctor, Derek was allowed to make the decision. "Let's first remember that he's a boy," said Dr. Stephen Anderson, a pediatric endocrinologist in Atlanta. "If he wants to go then we can choose between empowering him over this disease or sending him a message that it took a great chunk of fun out of his life."

A week later, Derek was providing his own self-care for a chronic disease halfway around the world. Of course, both his family and Derek knew that they needed to educate and prepare others who would be with him, so teachers and friends gathered at his house before the trip to make sure they knew what to look for and how to help him if needed. Derek had a blast, and one day while swimming off the Great Barrier Reef, his teacher looked at him from a distance and gave him the thumbs up sign as if to ask, "Everything OK?" Derek unzipped his pack, grabbed his glucose gel and gave the thumbs up right back with a smile.

Derek recalls the experience as a true catalyst, fueled by the conviction from his parents that he could fit diabetes into his life. "My parents have done a really good job of setting reasonable expectations for diabetes management while still letting me maintain a life of independence," he says. He was also fortunate in that he was still in the honeymoon phase that made management for him much smoother. "I had little fluctuation; it was actually quite easy in Australia," he said. It also set the tone for a lifelong approach to his diabetes care: He would not be prevented from living a normal life. That's become Derek's story. Like many others, that story has freed and focused him to live a life with no boundaries, only opportunities, and he's making the most of it.

In Derek's Words

"I don't want it, but it won't prevent me from living a normal life."

A QUICK START

From an early age, Derek was interested in the sciences. "Science came really easy to me," Derek says. It stood out even more for Derek when he realized that outside of sports, other interests didn't capture him the way the sciences did. While at The Lovett School, a premier and prestigious college preparatory institution in Atlanta, Derek took courses in environmental science, physics, AP Biology, organic chemistry and biochemistry. He played a number of sports growing up, including baseball, soccer and football, but found a passion for squash, above all.

They say in sports that it is always good to get off to a strong start. Maintaining that and following through are a different matter, but coming out of the gate strong puts you on the right track and creates the conditions favorable for a great outcome. The

Lovett School provided that for Derek because he was already a creative and critical thinker, and the school drove his intellectual curiosity. By the time Derek was accepted into Stanford University, he had a pretty good idea about his plans for the immediate future: squash. For his longer-term future, he chose medical school. He was also the financial manager of the men's squash team, and would become their captain in his senior year. That sounded like a full schedule to me until he added that he was also a resident assistant for both his dorm in junior year and his fraternity in senior year, handling everything from upperclassmen's academic needs to their personal and emotional challenges on top of leading weekly meetings, managing and hiring personnel and handling finances. He was now doing at 21 what he first was doing in pre-school— leading and empathizing—just on a higher plane.

In only his second year at Stanford, Derek co-created and co-lead a student initiated course called Human Biology 19SI—"Introduction to Stem Cells: A Multi-disciplinary Perspective." It was a weekly lecture series for stem cell professionals to present their area of expertise, be it scientific, legal, ethical or entrepreneurial.

He also didn't waste any time becoming active in his areas of interest while at the same time broadening his experience and exposure. It's not easy to be a standout at Stanford and Derek knew he would need to continually improve and push himself outside his direct areas of competency. He worked as a financial analyst during the summer leading into his sophomore year and also worked as a psychophysiology research assistant in the Stanford psychology department, where he worked on projects designed to better understand how rewarding certain coping mechanisms could improve psychological outcomes.

STARTING TO MAKE A DIFFERENCE

It was his early experience at Stanford, though, that opened Derek's eyes to opportunities to make a difference beyond practicing medicine alone. "Stanford exposes you and forces you to experience entrepreneurship," he says. "Everyone you know is involved with or has an idea for a startup." Many people who go to Stanford are already interested in entrepreneurship or quickly become interested due to the excitement, enthusiasm and participation of students in the multitude of opportunities available on campus. Derek got a true taste of that by the end of his sophomore year with his first entrepreneurial opportunity at Avva Health, Inc., where he began to leverage his myriad strengths.

That opportunity came with a friend from Derek's fraternity, Aris Theologis. They had a lot in common: two parents who were physicians, an incredible intellect and passion for medicine, and a desire to pursue life sciences outside of practicing medicine as a physician. Derek recognized this as an amazing opportunity for him to be introduced to the world of life sciences entrepreneurship. "I knew Aris was an incredibly smart guy, he was set to go to Harvard Business School on a specialized program, our passions were aligned, and I knew he was an amazing guy to learn from," Derek said. At the time, Aris had an idea for developing an online navigation tool that could help breast cancer patients and survivors manage their care and treatment. The tool was designed to help newly diagnosed patients answer questions about their disease, manage their treatment roadmap, gain support from their connections and loved ones, and to keep track of the nurses and physicians that they would be interacting with. Finally, the tool helped survivors manage themselves following their treatment. Aris felt there was a need for this after he had an experience shadowing physicians at the Stanford Cancer Clinic. "I knew right away that I wanted to be involved," Derek said.

On top of his academic, sport and volunteer duties, Derek was now about to embark on his first major life sciences entrepreneurship opportunity that would begin to shape the direction his life would take. His role was to interact with breast cancer patients and survivors to help them maximize the utility of the online tool. He conducted patient interviews to guide product features. He analyzed and distilled those interviews to inform the effectiveness of overall breast management practices. His one-on-one work with patients was supplemented with marketing and advertising experience in which he developed partnerships with local breast cancer organizations and physicians to recruit Avva's patient pool, personally recruiting more than 40 women to participate in their extensive market research program. He would also be instrumental in identifying and improving the user-interface experience through feedback sessions.

It was a challenging experience, but it was a real-life learning opportunity and gave Derek a window into business and business development, interfacing with users, entrepreneurship, technology, life sciences and managing a heavy demand schedule with multiple priorities. In Derek's junior year, he applied for the Mayfield Fellowship, a nine-month selective, highly competitive internship combining classroom education and real-world experience focused on entrepreneurship and innovation. Only 12 to 15 fellows are chosen annually. The fellowship is offered through the Stanford School of Engineering and was established with the entrepreneurship lens from an engineering perspective. As a result, "the majority of students are getting either a Bachelor of Science or some kind of engineering degree," Derek explains. Each year, they may take a few non-traditional students into the program. When the fellows in the 2011 class began, Derek Rowley was the one applicant accepted that did not come from the engineering school, and would set him on a path of future growth while establishing him as a top talent from a prestigious school.

The program is an incredible opportunity for an elite group of students to gain mentorship and insight into real-life business case studies led by prominent Stanford faculty members Tom Byers and Tina Selig, who guide, inform and facilitate discussion among the group of fellows. It wasn't solely focused on reading and reviewing material, either. Many times, people directly involved in real-life business situations would come in and speak to the class. It is the real-life experience and support that the Mayfield program provides that is truly so valuable. Derek had mentors in arenas such as venture capital and law, and recent alumni who were there to answer questions, guide his experience, and provide high-level support to make the most of the program. The Mayfield program truly stands alone in its prestigious reputation, mining and preparing the future's best talent by providing a mentor within a company a student can work with to gain access and insights that simply can't happen in the university setting. That mentor's main responsibility to the fellow is to ensure access to whomever and whatever will support their goals for the program. Derek had an exceptional mentor in Sejal Sheth at Pacific Biosciences, a next-generation DNA sequencing company exploring the next frontier in targeted medicine. "Sejal was incredible," Derek says enthusiastically. Sejal had previously married a Mayfield fellow so she was very knowledgeable about the program, which really helped Derek make the most of his experience. "She got me one-on-one C-level meetings every other week, and I was able to sit in on numerous meetings with those executives," Derek says, providing him a second-to-none experience with direct access and exposure to the world of start-up entrepreneurship in the sciences.

Derek's work at Pacific Biosciences was in the product marketing area, where he worked closely with Sejal and learned about strategy, product management, and company organizational structure. It was perfect for Derek, as they were areas of business outside his direct experience, further broadening his business base to add to his incredible medical and technical knowledge. His time at Pacific touched on the marketing and manufacturing sides as well, dealing in pricing, packaging and technical specifications around quality control.

DECIDING ON A PATH

It was an invaluable experience that created more questions than Derek may have anticipated, especially since he had always felt so confident about what he wanted to do when he first walked on to the Stanford campus—practice medicine.

Now, the main unanswered question was if he should go to medical school when he graduated. This was complicated by reflecting on his experience during those early years at Stanford, starting with Avva, where he began to consider how he could apply entrepreneurship to attacking the world's most pressing medical problems. "I did not want there to be any doubts about medical school," Derek said. He needed total conviction for that life plan and he didn't have it. What he did have was a clearer plan to play in an arena outside of anything he ever imagined. "My experience at Avva and Pacific Biosciences confirmed for me that I could be involved in providing a medical service without being a physician," Derek said. "There is an opportunity to do a lot of good in treating diseases even though you're not at the front line as a physician." Derek has a humble and honest way of honoring and valuing physician work, having come from a home with two parents as physicians who stimulated his interest in medicine while at the same time paying attention to what stirs inside of him—a deep hunger and drive to make a difference in the world. He has a great respect for physicians, as they are on the front line of patient care. What he knows, however, is that he can create a sense of purpose and passion by operating at levels that impact the doctor-patient relationship in a variety of ways, from empowering the patient in disease management to facilitating higher quality interaction between patient and physician.

It is my sense in getting to know Derek that while he would clearly be a great physician, his passion for business and technology to intersect with medicine can be a kind of holy grail for him to drive deeply necessary changes in health care and medicine in our country and the world. He only confirms this by adding: "If I can facilitate the doctor-patient exchange with something that I've done, I know that it will have a great impact in the world and give me a sense that I'm doing good."

By his senior year, Derek decided to apply for consulting jobs to take the first step in his newly articulated vision of leveraging his skills, knowledge, expertise and passion in health care. He would do it by gaining experience in the combined arena of business, entrepreneurship and medicine. Derek could do whatever he wanted and he now had the enviable task of trying to decide what direction his career path would take, a conundrum that anyone would jump at the chance to have. His experience at Stanford was so full and rich with multi-disciplinary activities and interests. The fact that he did all of that while managing his diabetes is not only a marvel, but deeply inspiring for anyone connected to this disease.

BALANCING DIABETES

Type 1 diabetes seems to be a constant trade-off between perfect management and living a rich and full life. The problem, as Derek points out, is trying to accomplish both without understanding there is a trade-off. "I can have close to perfect blood sugars if all I do every day is just manage my diabetes," Derek says. "That's not good enough for me, because there's a lot I want to do in life, so it's really about finding the proper balance between my management and how I can best fit it into my life." That is different for everyone, but what I value about Derek's viewpoint is that it's so balanced and realistic. He has also figured out how to make diabetes work in his life. He is not trying to be perfect so he doesn't experience the guilt associated with not achieving it. He is smart enough to know the level of care he requires, but he's equally interested in caring for his life, and at his young age, he's figured out a way to view the condition that is both empowering and realistic.

In Derek's Words

"It's easy to always want that 70 to 140 blood sugar, but it's just not realistic. If that's the narrow window that you are trying to arrive at in your diabetes management then you may often feel unsuccessful.… That can lead to a slippery slope to just complete negligence."

As physicians, Derek's parents knew that the medical attention that Derek needed was paramount, but they also knew that far-off complications were not the best motivator for present-day care. Derek recalls his father setting up incentives that both formed good habits and rewarded "in range" blood sugars. Since good effort does not always promise the desired result, Derek's father built in a two-tier incentive system to pay for half of Derek's car when he was getting set to drive. One tier was how many blood sugars were checked in a day. With that tier completed, he would be able to get to the next tier around actual results. What I love about that strategy is that it forms the necessary habits. Instead of putting the focus on what we all care about—the ultimate A1C—what Derek's parents focused on was the number of checks, since that is the true metric behind achieving a desired A1C. "Effort-based rewards are incredibly important, especially with diabetes because it's so unpredictable," Derek says. Without it, he advises, you can really lose control of your diabetes because your focus is on an outcome that you just can't entirely control.

His balanced approach to care came from balanced parenting as well. Derek's parents were very consistent in managing him, the only difference mainly being that his mother worried more. I relate to that since Tara is often more worried about Gavin than I am, so perhaps that's just a gender difference. I smile when Derek tells me that his mother still does her check-ins around how he's doing, how much he's traveling and when his next endocrinologist appointment is. What is clear, though, is the importance of parental consistency in terms of how you manage the disease to how you view the disease; that, in turn, will shape how your child manages and views his diabetes. Derek's parents have done an amazing job of instilling great habits for him to manage his condition while affording him the opportunity to truly be independent. He also has come to learn that there is another key responsibility of having type 1 diabetes—educating others about the disease.

He can talk about his type 1 experience with a keen understanding of not only what it's like to live and grow with the condition, but even more amazingly as someone who can empathize with those he interacts with who don't have it. He moves seamlessly between discussing his own condition and how it impacts other people. He's become adept at forming positive stories around what could easily bring on negative emotions. When he was asked if he should be eating certain things or when people presumed that factors in his lifestyle led to his diagnosis, he used to be very frustrated. Today, he understands that there is a great deal of confusion and lack of education around both type 1 and type 2 diabetes. Remember, Derek had to live for eight years as the child without diabetes and that experience has made him incredibly intuitive and understanding of the psychosocial impact that it has. As a result, he is very tolerant and is quick to point out to people the differences and that he, like millions of others, did nothing to get type 1 diabetes. They just have to figure out a way to live with it that works for them and their lives.

A BRIGHT FUTURE

Like many of the people featured in this book, Derek presents at such a high level of intellect and emotional awareness that it's hard to believe he's just 24. I have a deep sense of excitement for his future since it is so full of promise. I also know that when I was 24, I was barely even thinking about my future, let alone what kind of difference I could be making in the world. It took me years to talk about my life and future in the ways that Derek does now. In getting to know him, I believe that much of that is due to his family background, personal struggles, intellect and wonderful education. But I'm also now realizing that his diabetes never limited him; just the opposite, in fact. Derek's diabetes fueled his growth and success and will continue to do so.

Today, Derek is involved with some very progressive work at McKinsey & Company, one of the most prestigious consulting firms in the world. He is excited to be working in his direct area of interest doing strategy work for medical products and operations improvements for large health care providers. It's further confirmation for him that medical school was not the right option for him, that he is best suited to advancing business and science to make a difference for doctors and patients alike. While his future is bright, one of the most exciting aspects of being so young is that we don't yet know what or where Derek Rowley's future will take him. What we do know is that he will be in control of it, and whatever it looks like it will have a lofty purpose, focused on the greater good. That's been Derek's whole life—helping people and doing good, adding value to the world.

No one knows for sure what the future will hold, but Derek believes his will be in the area of managing chronic disease. Derek lives every day with a chronic disease, but it also holds a great deal of intellectual challenge that can always stimulate his curiosity and ability to solve tough medical problems. What Derek shares with me about his future, I also realize, is an insight into my view of managing diabetes for Gavin—integrating management into your life. "How do you most efficiently empower someone to take control of their disease and how does that taking control become not yet another impediment to their daily living?" he asks. For Derek, the challenge is how to integrate daily living with disease management to make it one and the same so it doesn't feel like something else you have to be doing. The integration into your life of managing a chronic disease, I've learned, is a way to avoid burnout and live a life in which you can achieve anything you want. It's been Derek's life experience so it doesn't surprise me that this may very well be at the heart of Derek's work, since that is exactly who he is—integrated and whole.

BARBARA ANDERSON

Professor of Pediatrics and Associate Head of Psychology
Baylor College of Medicine

BARBARA ANDERSON HAS SPENT 30 YEARS WORKING IN THE FIELD of type 1 diabetes. She has helped thousands of families along the way, working at four of this country's premier diabetes centers, including Joslin Diabetes Center in Boston. She teaches pediatrics and is associate head of psychology at Baylor College of Medicine in Houston.

Barbara has seen much of what we all go through as either diagnosed or as parents, friends and siblings of loved ones with type 1. One of the major contributing factors to her success in working with type 1 families is her special ability (I'd call it a gift) to really listen to people.

Barbara swiftly and with great authenticity can soothe a person and get to the heart of what really matters. Her philosophy is simple: Patients will take better care of themselves when their doctors take time to understand and respect them. In an address to the American Diabetes Association when she won its Outstanding Educator in Diabetes Award, Barbara compared her method to that of a horse whisperer who uses tactics such as learning a horse's natural language to understand and respect the innate nature of the horse.

THE DISEASE BURDEN

Barbara's understanding of type 1 begins with what she calls "The Disease Burden." She recounts a story about a young woman in a university environment who was using control solution and her roommate's blood to fake better blood glucose results. Another student, a smart and motivated chemistry major (no less) was burned out from blood glucose checking because she had never been able to please her parents or doctors. So she stopped monitoring her blood glucose when she went to college. Then there was the story of a teenager whose parents would yell at him for having blood glucose levels over 200 or for not checking his blood sugar often enough.

None of these parents or patients are "bad" or "mentally ill." These parents love their children and are scared of complications, but they need help in finding more effective ways to encourage self-care in their teens with type 1 diabetes.

The stories go on and on. We all know that diabetes in our homes goes well beyond the physical needs and challenges of a chronic condition. There are the tools we always think of to manage the physical aspects of type 1, like the pumps, meters, CGMs (continuous glucose monitors) and tracking software. Then there are emotional and mental tools to grapple with this condition and emerge as resilient families and resilient young adults with type 1. What does type 1 diabetes do to those diagnosed? How does it impact loved ones? Most especially, how does that influence our most important relationships? What I truly like about Barbara is that she recognizes that we must understand the problem before we can begin to fix it. So, what's the real problem here? She characterizes it in the simple term: "The Disease Burden."

It starts with recognition and awareness, because we can't influence what we don't notice or recognize as a problem. "Many families are in knots," she says pointedly. Barbara's candor is at the same time empowering and sobering.

In Barbara's Words

"We need to talk about the fact that there is a *disease burden*. Type 1 diabetes is at best tedious and at worst, always changing and in fluctuation, and vacation is not an option."

The fact is, as Barbara explains, that there is very little praise or positivity in diabetes care. "It's emotionally exhausting," she says. "*You can do everything right and not get it right.* That is why we need to look at and reward behavior (the act of checking BGs [blood glucose levels]), not the outcome (the number on the meter)."

A Personal View:
Focus on the Behavior, Not the Outcome

What a game changer that is. I remember a golf pro teaching my dad and me some very specific lessons about putting. He said, "All you can control is the speed and the line of the putt you want. You can't control the ball going in the hole." I thought it was a great life lesson at the time as well. John Wooden, the legendary UCLA coach who earned 12 NCAA titles, said that all you can control is effort, not winning. If people do their best they will still fall short some of the time. Not surprisingly, though, it's those same people who persist and put out the best effort that win most of the time.

Barbara makes it clear that we have the game wrong. Reward the effort, not the blood glucose reading.

One parent told his son that he would raise his allowance if he kept his blood sugar reading under a certain number. With the best intentions, he was potentially setting up his son for disappointment. What if the boy checked himself numerous times and injected the right amounts of insulin, but happened to be going through a growth spurt or a particularly stressful time or any other number of combinations of things in the imperfect science that influences blood sugar levels? Should he be scolded or not rewarded for that effort? How many times have you fallen short despite your best efforts? Think about times taking care of your loved one … did you always get it right?

A Personal View: The Ongoing Challenge

One time, Gavin's blood sugar was 54 and I gave him carbohydrates to treat the low. I did not give him an insulin shot, despite giving him carbohydrates that warranted additional insulin.

Emotionally, the low on this particular day caused me to not act. Maybe I didn't want to give him yet another shot. Maybe I justified it by saying how much exercise he had that day. Or, maybe I was just burned out and hoping for the best. Yet two and a half hours later, Gavin's blood sugar was 324. When I saw that number, I played the conversation back in my head, this time with more awareness and attention as to why I did what I did. The fact is that he needed more insulin, given the carbs that I gave him earlier to treat the low. I told myself that, because he had been super low, he probably wouldn't go that high, and I didn't want to give him a shot soon after experiencing a low.

I've learned from that experience. This disease is powerful in the stories we can tell ourselves. I try the best I can now to treat based on ratios and corrections, and take my stories out of it. It's an ongoing challenge.

We are well-meaning, concerned and worried, but we are imperfect; the new technologies available to help *manage* (NOT *control*) blood sugar levels are also not perfect tools, and as a result, we cannot expect perfection. Barbara is adept at re-socializing people into diabetes; she feels that everyone deserves a "fresh start." Here's what we need to remember the most: "The burden is on the kids," she says. "It is so punishing for kids worried about repercussions." She so gently reminds me that we don't hound our kids when they have a temperature and it would be unimaginable for a child going through chemotherapy to be blamed for their cancer, "but this is how we respond with type 1. It's another disease, one the child is not responsible for getting, yet many times they have to deal with feelings of guilt or blaming themselves."

We don't reward or encourage how much effort and energy it takes. Burnout happens and it wears you down. "*There is no other disease where the patient is responsible for their own care*," she says. What an awesome responsibility that is. People with type 1 diabetes need to know this.

A Personal View

On a family vacation, I was getting ready to give Gavin a shot and for the first time he ran away from me. I hadn't prepared myself for this almost certain eventuality. My conversation with Barbara helped immensely. Although Gavin was only 4 at the time, I looked him in the eye and said, "I know it's not easy. You have to put up with a lot and you're not even sure why. That's OK. You are as tough as they come. You have to get your finger pricked and get shots each and every day and I want you to know how strong you are and how much I love you." With tears in my eyes I could see his sense of pride lift though he didn't say anything. He took his shot and made me chase him home from the park giggling the whole way there. I'll never forget it.

Barbara is about giving people the tools to provide a fresh start, to suggest another way of thinking and acting around type 1 diabetes that may be more satisfying and lighten your load. I know that is welcome for all of us.

It's not Barbara's accomplished background or how much she's published or even that she holds challenging jobs in pediatrics and psychology at Baylor that give me confidence in her experience (although that clearly helps!). It's her warmth, encouragement and knowledge that we need to pay more attention to the mental and emotional elements of type 1 diabetes if we're going to have resilient relationships and families that stay strong and healthy. It seems evident to me that there is so much going on in the background that is unseen and unspoken about how we all are dealing with managing our own or someone else's condition. Until we shine a light on the disease burden, then we will struggle to empower those with type 1 to feel inspired to live their lives while staying motivated to manage their diabetes.

It's worth sharing four powerful strategies from Barbara that can act as a catalyst to addressing the disease burden and its related challenges. It can be found in the *power of language, the muzzle rule, the cost-benefit ratio* and finally, right in your *local community*.

THE POWER OF LANGUAGE

It's not what you say, it's what they hear.

Don't guess, test! Have you heard that clever expression on PSAs educating people that testing is their best chance at managing your diabetes? While clever and filled with the best intentions, this campaign has a huge language problem.

As Barbara pointed out to me, part of what contributes to our anxiety around type 1 care is the usage of the word "test." If we're always being tested than that means we're always passing or failing. This has huge implications for how we perceive our experience in managing diabetes, and mostly it sets us up for chronic worrying. If you're *checking or monitoring* yourself, then you are trying to get a current reading of your blood sugar as a source of valuable information. It's not to determine failure, mediocrity or success, albeit fleeting. By checking blood sugar, we can incorporate that information into a future action. Not good, bad or indifferent, just information.

If you look at a blood glucose reading as information and not a grade, are you more likely to avoid the emotional roller coaster? "YES!" Barbara says. A blood sugar reading is a way to guide, inform and help navigate the complexities that diabetes presents. Frankly, I'm thankful that we can get an instant reading (see Rob Campbell on page 79)! It's not to make us feel bad about what we did or didn't do, or to temporarily make us feel good if we're in range. Think about this. If you get a number in range, do you celebrate it? No, you just move on because you know it will change. Why don't we do that when we get a low or high reading? It is just information, after all. How we perceive that information shapes our emotions. Our emotions are our reality and again, are influenced by the language we use and the stories we tell. Barbara emphasizes that parents need to know that an out-of-range blood glucose level does not equal complications, and that over-reacting to an out of-range level never helps blood glucose get back in range.

The words we use are critical to our emotional and mental state. How we feel profoundly influences our performance and our relationships with others. How do you feel when you get a blood sugar out of range? Do the words "angry" or "frustrated" come to mind? Do you feel disappointed or let down? Shape your own reality by choosing words that better meet reasonable expectations. Parents can be incredibly hard on their kids and themselves, and individuals can learn to be hard on themselves. We need to be more positive about what it truly takes to manage a daily life condition, a preferred word over disease. It's not suppressing or denying the negative aspects of type 1, but it's clear we spend too much time on the negative or put too much pressure on ourselves or loved ones. Loosen the rein a bit if you can, choose better words and you can experience a better journey.

A Personal View

I found myself feeling challenged and frustrated by the percentage of time we were "out of range." I decided to ask the doctor what a reasonable range is for a 4 year old. He said 100 to 200. Now, that clearly doesn't mean that I want Gavin up close to 200, but I also know not to beat myself up if he has numbers at that level or even higher. I also opened up the numbers to 80 to 200. My language is now about a zone, not a range. It feels better to not have to worry about being "out of range." That feels like failure. I just want him in the zone as much as possible and we don't worry about when he's not because that's just information to help us get him back in the zone!

THE MUZZLE RULE

This simple and powerful rule is based on a key philosophy that Barbara feels can not only improve relationships and ease family conflict, but also has been shown to consistently help children and adolescents check themselves enough or more often! As it turns out that's what we want more than anything.

"Parents have a right to know their children's blood sugars," she says. "What they don't have a right to is to berate, harass, criticize, blame or guilt their children based on those numbers."

The Muzzle Rule is a two-week strategy whereby the child promises to show his/her parents their numbers. The parent promises to have no reaction (easier written than done). At the end of two weeks, the parents and child come together to discuss their experience with this strategy. Barbara's most typical reactions:

Child: "This was incredible. I had no fear or worry about how my parents might react to one blood sugar so I could check myself without all the other stuff that comes with my condition."

Parent: "This was really tough, but my child is checking more and what I learned at the end of this is that's what I really want. To make sure she's on top of it. Now we're able to help her focus on the most important thing, how to make sure she's getting enough insulin in a way that fits into her life without worrying about disappointing us or making us angry."

What I love about this rule is that it unleashes the deep-residing, good intentions of parents. It's clear to me that both time and the constant worry about a loved one in a chronic condition conspire to make parents do "not good things," as Barbara puts it. Of course parents love and want the best for their child. The problem is that fear gets in the way, shuts down our rational thinking and promotes the very things we're trying to defend against: further alienation in the relationship and an inattention to the disease as a form of retaliation.

It's called *miscarried helping* and it's a psychological term for when we unknowingly sabotage the very thing we're trying to develop. Recently, my wife bought a beautiful plant that we had out on our patio. At the arboretum, they told her that it needs a lot of water and plenty of sun to stay healthy, particularly in the early stages. Have you ever watered a plant too much? Well, you know what happens. It shrivels, fights for life and tries to overcome an abundance of the very ingredient it needs the most.

We all want to nurture our children, and like plants, give them plenty of water and sunshine. We need to make sure we're not sabotaging what we want by being so intrusive and overly worried that we end up suffocating and sabotaging the very thing we're trying to develop with our children. What's needed is a balance of enough water, sunshine and room to grow, leading to a healthy relationship and a healthy child.

Focus on the goal, not the fear.

THE COST-BENEFIT RATIO

The cost-benefit ratio has long been used as a business financial analysis to determine if the cost of something is truly worth the benefits or the upside. It can also be a wildly useful tool to use in our own lives as a check in. Is the price I'm paying for something truly worth the benefit I perceive I am getting? Simply put, is it worth it? To help answer that question, we need an honest assessment about what's needed in caring for type 1 and an understanding of the costs and benefits in our own or someone else's care.

There's a lot of gray area in diabetes. You don't have to have the disease or care for it for very long to appreciate that. As a result, let's start with the one thing that we truly do know: People with type 1 diabetes need insulin to live and prevent complications. Everything else is secondary. What I mean by secondary is how you get the insulin, how it fits into an individual's life, what doctor you work with, if you follow a meal plan or count carbohydrates and a myriad of other decisions related to the condition. In other words, we have choices and we're not fixed or tied to any particular plan, just what works for us! "Don't fight over the options," Barbara says. "It's important to recognize that we all want to prevent complications, but at what cost are we doing that?" Barbara feels strongly that just because there are all sorts of products on the market, it doesn't mean we have to use them all. There is more to the complications of diabetes than potential vision loss, neuropathy, kidney disease or other physical dangers. There are huge emotional complications as well, such as guilt, anxiety, worry, poor self-esteem and overall feelings of inadequacy. We want our young adults with type 1 to be resilient and move on with their dreams while staying motivated to manage type 1.

~~~~~~

A Personal View: We Have Options

When Gavin first started using the pump in January, 2010, we felt that a huge burden had been lifted from us. Being able to bolus in a moment's notice for a young, finicky eater, having the ability to lower his basal insulin if he started going low during his bedtime check, and the diminished intrusiveness overall from elimination of the daily five to six shots meant that this disease would somehow be made easier to contend with. Add to that the perception of tighter glucose control and it's easy to justify that it's a win for the child and for the parent. The costs of an intrusive, painful and emotionally upsetting period for all of us during site changes didn't seem to outweigh these enormous benefits.

We were on the pump for about 14 months when we started having challenges. Gavin was no longer absorbing insulin as well as he had been (or so it seemed) and our product manufacturer really couldn't help us figure it out, so we received a new pump. Once again, after two days on a new site change we would see numbers dramatically rise. As summer rolled around, we noticed that the pump site was always compromised when he went in the pool. Our frustration grew. We tried to figure out all the issues, but it just wasn't working like before and the costs started to exceed the benefits of the pump. Since we really did enjoy having him on the pump, we tried defiantly to troubleshoot, examine, question and work on a solution.

Finally, with the absorption challenge coupled with the infusion set being pulled out each time he went into the pool, we decided to move him back to insulin shots, just like how we started. It seemed like a big step backward. We were worried about keeping him in as tight a blood sugar range (our own worry, not proven at all). We didn't want Gavin to have to put up with all the shots again, and—now having known the convenience of the pump—we were frustrated by having to go back to what seemed to be an outdated management tool for this condition.

Almost immediately, we were enjoying the new benefits of making sure that insulin was getting into our little boy. He was just getting to the age where he could begin to communicate, so we asked him. "Hey Gav, do you want pump or shots?" Not once did he say pump. We have not looked back.

Tara and I learned a valuable lesson that summer. In diabetes care there's what the caretakers want, but there's another party to consider here and one much more important: the one who actually has to live with this disease burden. If you have a family member or friend with diabetes, how often have you asked them how it's going? What their challenges are? What could be different that may make their experience smoother and more satisfying? People have been asking us how his A1C is now that he's off the pump and back on shots. Well, we're happy to report that he's doing as well and occasionally even better. He's been averaging an A1C of 6.5 whether on shots or pump.

"There is no evidence currently of the pump being better than shots for young children," Barbara says. Our family is a clear example of that. Not only have his numbers often been in the zone, but he also prefers that tubing not be attached to him and that he doesn't have to wear a special belt every day. That's him. For someone else it's completely different. They probably prefer not having multiple shots and don't mind the small matter of wearing a pump. What's important is that it works for their lives, not just for ours.

~~~~~~

As most new parents dealing with the disease, we want all the things that may help us manage it. We had spoken to several people about CGMs that can give you almost instantaneous glucose readings and how they are trending. The cost to pay for this benefit is an additional weekly insertion of a sensor (with a needle), usually in the abdomen, to continuously monitor glucose levels. We tried the product for one week and when we inserted the sensor into Gavin, it was clear to Tara and me that there were going to have to be some huge benefits to make this worth it.

It was a painful and traumatic experience for him. He didn't want to take his shirt off. He was self-conscious and you could tell he was burned out on the various things that could enter his skin on a regular basis. We decided at the end of that week that the CGM, despite its wonderful benefits and intentions, was not worth the cost. The CGM was clearly an emotionally traumatic and upsetting experience for him, and he was constantly reminded of it by looking down at this relatively large device on his little tummy.

Now, for some, the CGM does not have this kind of impact, although Barbara shares with me that she finds that most people who use CGMs effectively are adults. "Don't crucify children with tools," she says. "We need more tools than meters and CGMs."

What we all should know is that there are work-around solutions. We can achieve our goals without the costs outweighing the benefits. We can get confused with all the claims of meter accuracy, quicker-acting insulin, this pump or that pump, the latest CGM and all the other issues that constantly bark at us … are you doing all you can do to make sure you or your loved one are preventing complications of this chronic condition? It's time to simplify. The bottom line is that the patient needs insulin. After that, make sure the benefits outweigh the costs and that starts with the opinions and voice of the diagnosed, not what makes it easier for us or gives us a false sense of an improved A1C. We have choices, but we need to listen to ourselves and our loved ones. What's the best fit for you that ensures the delivery of insulin? "We need a new way of thinking that includes other perspectives and that empowers the individual," Barbara says.

LOCAL COMMUNITY

The sharing of a burden can be one of the most helpful tools in reducing its impact.

In the many stories I have researched, I've noticed a consistent theme: Having a shared sense of community is one of the most empowering ways to deal with the disease burden and carry on with a purposeful spirit.

"It's so important to get people talking who have a shared burden because it really helps people know they have support and that they are not alone," Barbara says.

There are local JDRF and ADA groups, websites, blogs, walks, events and so many other ways to connect with those in your community who can relate to you on levels that very few people in your life ever will. They are numerous and everywhere. They're great for those supporting others with type 1 as well as those who share the condition. Many of the stories shared in this book also convey the sense of connecting with the community. Morgan Patton (page 94) had no reason to turn it around until she found a sense of a community or shared interest. For Rob Campbell (page 79), his experiences at camps and Joslin fueled his excitement to overcome and give back.

Our family has found it through JDRF meetings, getting involved with outreach committees and participating in annual walks. We have met some amazing people who don't have to ask one question to understand. We all know how misunderstood type 1 diabetes can be. (One woman once told Tara assuredly that Gavin should be able to take a pill for his condition.) Most people just don't get it, which makes having friends and a community that shares your experience, well, so less lonely.

After I thank Barbara profusely for her time and insights, she exclaims that she is privileged to work with families who are open and looking for better ways to manage this disease burden.

What needs to change? What can we be doing better? "We have a long way to go in helping doctors understand they don't need to put fear into people to get them to respond," she says. Many health care providers (MDs, NPs, CDEs, RDs, psychologists) would benefit from understanding that fear is not a sustainable motivator of self-care in those living with diabetes. There are great doctors out there who understand that type 1 diabetes is not just about the physical needs, but the emotional and mental needs as well, in order for people to live complete lives.

We all deserve that and it's up to us to demand it. Barbara reminds and reinforces for me that if you want people to feel empowered and hopeful, you need to encourage them, invest in them and understand their lives. Most doctors would probably tell you they don't have time for that. As a result, we shouldn't have time for those doctors.

Barbara has been a pediatric psychologist working with families living with type 1 diabetes for 30 years. One person asked her if it gets boring. Barbara, in her kindest of ways could not dismiss this absurdity with a scoff. Instead, with a smile, she said, "Not at all. I learn so much from every family that I see. And I believe that I'm making an impact and helping children thrive."

Yes, you are, Barbara. And we are incredibly grateful.

FINAL THOUGHTS:
A DEVELOPING STORY

THE STORIES YOU JUST READ HAVE SWITCHED SOMETHING ON IN me that has fueled my passion to join others and make sure that the dreams and aspirations of all those diagnosed with type 1 come to life. As our Diabetes Dad, Tom Karlya, reminds us, "Just don't do nothing."

I invite you, for a moment, to consider the stories of those who deal with type 1 in the developing world. Their stories are startlingly different.

Imagine a world where children and adolescents are dying of diabetes or at best are chronically unwell. Imagine diabetes impacting a person's ability to complete school, find a job or get married. Imagine not being able to afford insulin and having to let your child die of diabetes so you can afford to feed the rest of your family. Now, imagine that this is happening today and every day in developing countries from the Caribbean islands to the Middle East, India and Africa.

In Nepal, Ashok KC, 16, was diagnosed with type 1 diabetes at the age of 12. He commutes two hours by bus to get to Patan Hospital. He must go monthly or his insulin will spoil. He can't eat at school, and most upsetting to him, he can't just go where he wants. He's on a regimented diet. That is, when he has food.

His story and others about children struggling with diabetes in impoverished Nepal families are told in Academy Award nominee Edward Lachman's 2007 *Life for a Child* documentary. Other stories in the film include that of Anupa, a 6-year-old type 1 girl whose walk to the bus with her father takes four hours if her blood sugar is under control, six hours if not. There's also the story of the family who had to give up their home and land to move closer to the hospital so their baby boy could access insulin. The family now works for a landowner taking care of his water buffalo, their days filled with hard labor. The mother, who completely understands her predicament, in a terrifyingly truthful manner says, "This is struggle, isn't it?"

Every day in the developing world these events are happening. The film isn't a look-at-them-to-make-us-feel-better story. We are all part of the diabetes community, but so often we don't hear or think enough about this part of our community. They, too, are part of the diabetes family, and they are truly struggling. In our world, those diagnosed with type 1 diabetes can do so many things when the condition is under control. In the developed world, those with type 1 are riddled with I can'ts. And that is not an excuse, it's the basis of their reality. It's hard to imagine that diabetes care could be so difficult in the developing world as we manage diabetes in the cushy Western world where monthly insulin shipments arrive at doors in cold packs and we find ourselves complaining about a testing error on our meters.

The International Diabetes Federation (IDF) estimates there are approximately 490,000 children in the world under the age of 15 with type 1 diabetes. However, the estimates for children and youth in many developing countries is uncertain due to lack of data as many children die undiagnosed. Many other children die, often within a year, due to a lack of insulin, expert medical care or diabetes education. Insulin was discovered in 1921, and nearly a century later there are still people dying who cannot access it.

The number of people in need of urgent care is estimated to be between 80,000 to 100,000 according to the IDF website. The

IDF is doing something about this devastating loss of life and opportunity. "No child should die of diabetes," says Dr. Graham Ogle, an Australian pediatric endocrinologist, citing the IDF's "Life for a Child" vision. Dr. Ogle is the general manager of the program, which provides everything from diabetes education and technical support for health professionals to sufficient insulin and blood glucose monitoring equipment that would be completely unaffordable to these patients.

AN ONGOING JOURNEY, YOUR STORY

The Life for a Child program recognizes that there are needy children who should not be dying of a disease for which there is medicine. This is a side of the story that we typically don't hear, but it's a powerful example that there are stories of diabetes everywhere. Stories of struggle, stories of hope, but overall stories of perseverance. Ashok KC has dreams of becoming a teacher. Anupa wants to be a nurse one day so she can help take care of others just like her. She figured out at the age of 6 in a poor and isolated area of Nepal what many people don't figure out in a lifetime: Take care of yourself so you can be at greater capacity to give back and take care of others.

What this program has in common with the stories you've just read is simple. The subjects of this book each have deeply held values and a strong sense of purpose beyond their own immediate interest. It clearly serves as a powerful source of fuel for their lives.

Stories are a combination of all of our previous experiences, knowledge and belief systems. Because they get embedded at an early age, it's important from time to time to challenge our stories, to upgrade them and to continue to make sure that they are serving us.

Additionally, the science of our own stories can also be a powerful force for why we do what we do and give us insight into how much more control we have over our emotions than we may think. In an insightful article by Benedict Carey in *The New York Times*, he celebrates and honors the career of one of the great brain researchers, Dr. Michael Gazzaniga, now 73.

Dr. Gazzaniga studied patients who had surgery to reduce seizures that involved cutting the connections between their left and right brain hemispheres. He was curious if the surgery had an effect on the patient.

In one study that Carey cites, Dr. Gazzaniga flashed a picture of a bicycle to the right hemisphere only. When split-brain patients were asked what they saw, they said, "Nothing." Since the left hemisphere, the seat of language, was disconnected, it got no visual input from the right hemisphere. The right hemisphere, which "saw" the bike, had no language to name it. The findings demolished the theory that specific functions were uniformly supported in the brain. Left brain/right brain became common language.

Dr. Gazzaniga's findings and subsequent discoveries about the brain offer all of us, particularly those with type 1 diabetes, a roadmap for understanding how we may respond to adversity and challenging circumstances. Through ongoing studies in the 1980s and 1990s, it became clear that the left hemisphere takes what information it has and delivers a clear story to conscious awareness. It happens all the time in our lives where we are constantly filling in blanks with assumptions so we can make facts into coherent stories. As humans, we are meaning-making machines. As Carey writes, we narrate our lives, shading every last detail, and even changing the script depending on the event, most of the time subconsciously. The stories never really stop, except perhaps during deep sleep. We must have meaning in what happens to us so we know how to behave, respond or assimilate—to make sense of our world.

So, if we are diagnosed with a disease, the left hemisphere has to give you a narration. I remember for us, the initial story produced was how much our life would change, and how Gavin may never experience the freedom from a chronic disease. Our hearts ached for him, for us, and the story quickly became "Why us?" The diagnosis was so powerful that it put us into fear mode and that was our initial story. Now, our story is we will do whatever it takes to overcome this *condition*, and in the process, never have it be a limiting factor for Gavin. It now even goes deeper. Type 1 diabetes will give Gavin the skills and capacity to accomplish whatever he wants because of the challenges inherent to the condition—resilience, fortitude, preparation, persistence, patience and empathy among many others. Not bad 21st century qualities for success and happiness.

We are also in a better position to tell more optimistic stories if we know more. The *Life for a Child* story shook me as a reminder of how basic some of the things that we take for granted truly are. There are people who wonder when their next insulin might come or if they will be able to live a life without constant struggle. Without this understanding, I would not be as appreciative or grateful about the care I am able to provide our son.

YOUR STORY

What an experience this has been. With each individual conversation, I felt more empowered, more confident and have a greater sense of joy for my child that anything is possible, somehow more possible, if you have type 1.

At the beginning, I was anxious about this project. Could I finish it? Could I do justice to all of my participants? Would I truly be able to get the story across and communicated in a way that could be helpful? Could I get to some of these great people? And probably, most of all, could I give our son something that could last a lifetime, not only in my willingness and drive to do this, but to do it in a way that could help him and millions like him thrive with this condition?

I'm so proud that the answers to these questions have been a resounding "Yes." Yes, you can. That's what I want to say to all those who have read this book. Yes, you can. You can have a life filled with promise and opportunity where type 1 diabetes plays in the background and has a constant role in your preparation, but never determines an outcome.

Most of all, what I recognized as I heard these stories is there are so many more like them. These inspiring stories are from incredible people and even they would tell you represent a great many more doing incredible things every day to overcome type 1. I have already been jotting down names and notes for my next book, as there are so many more people doing amazing things to overcome the chronic condition of type 1 diabetes.

With that, I also invite your stories. We all need them and I want to hear and share them among our community—a community of the most inspiring, encouraging, resilient and determined people I know.

Please go to **www.mytypecast.com** and tell us your stories or those you think can help others gain the insights they might need to flip their switch. The switch is there for everyone. It's just a matter if it's been switched on yet.

It's not just the stories we hear that motivate and inspire us. The most powerful ones are the stories we tell ourselves in our everyday self talk and the kinds of questions we ask in our own minds. It took Dr. Gazzaniga years to figure out that the competing voices of the brain are from a running narration provided by somewhere in the left hemisphere. He refers to the left hemisphere as "the interpreter." It suggests that we have the power to shape the interpretation of whatever happens to us. It just requires awareness about your stories. Are they proactive, curious and hopeful? Or, are they limiting, negative and confining? Go ahead, pay attention to yourself. The awareness you build will move you in the direction of your dreams because we can't influence what we don't see. One of the preeminent experts on story, author Robert McKee, comments that stories are how the mind absorbs, sorts and structures reality. So, make it a good one! The stories we tell are the most powerful impetus for the feelings we have. Why is that important? Our feelings are our life. How we feel profoundly influences our health, our relationships, our performance and fuels our purpose.

What's your story?

IT WILL NEVER BE HARDER TO HAVE TYPE 1 DIABETES THAN IT IS today. Tomorrow, and each day going forward, we can look to new technology, advances in medicine, increased funding for research and improved, more reliable data that make managing this condition easier. Yet, we know it is not easy.

Type 1 diabetes is a physically, emotionally and mentally challenging condition. One of the main challenges is that it is always there, never ceasing, reminding us in a variety of ways that we need to be constantly vigilant or there could be negative consequences. It requires so much of us, and on such a constant basis, that it's truly no wonder why terms such as "disease burden" are part of our language.

What seems simple in terms of matching insulin to blood sugar levels is as much art as it is science. Sometimes, despite our best efforts, we go unrewarded, in many cases having to take consecutive misses before we ever feel like we got it right. Type 1 diabetes is an obsessive disease because it requires constant monitoring. I have learned, sometimes the hard way, that obsession is the enemy. While the tools we have now are so great to help us manage, we must remember that they can also make us obsess even more from constantly peeking at the CGM to trying to figure out why the same meal after the same event had a 100-point swing. We must also remember that, while we need to manage as best we can, it does not do us any good to obsess about outcomes or yet another low.

Type 1 diabetes shows us that it touches all of us in every way possible, every ounce of our being. What I learned, most of all, is that perfect control is a fool's game. We can, however, always be improving yet still be satisfied with where we are. Better control is more sustainable of an approach than perfect control.

We may be much better served with this condition to manage closely from a distance. Do the best we can, and let go. Sprint and recover. The disease is a marathon, but if we run it like a sprint we'll drop in mile 1. Find your ways to let go and replenish yourself so you can engage with your condition and your life refreshed, poised, focused and purposeful—just as so many in these pages have done.

BIOGRAPHIES

PHIL SOUTHERLAND

Phil Southerland is the founder and CEO of Team Type 1, now called Team Novo Nordisk. Diagnosed at just 7 months old with type 1 diabetes, doctors told his mother he would probably go blind, suffer organ failure and likely not live past the age of 25. Now 31 and actively in control of his diabetes through diet, exercise and a disciplined insulin regimen, Southerland has turned what was once considered a death sentence into a global movement to positively affect the lives of people with diabetes worldwide through managed care and control of the disease.

An avid cyclist with a vision of using his bike as a tool for empowerment, Southerland established Team Type 1 in 2005, creating the world's first professional cycling team to include athletes with diabetes. Under his leadership, the squad rapidly grew into an enterprise of more than 100 athletes from 11 countries, spanning the globe to inspire and unite people affected with diabetes. The team's ultimate goal is to race on the sport's largest stage, the Tour de France. In May 2011, Southerland released a memoir titled *Not Dead Yet.*

For more information on Phil Southerland and Team Novo Nordisk, visit **www.teamnovonordisk.com** or follow him on Twitter **@philsoutherland**.

RICH HOLLENBERG

Rich can be seen and heard on the ESPN family of networks, calling college basketball games on ESPN, ESPN2 and ESPNU. He is also a reporter for NFL Network. A native of New Jersey currently living in St. Petersburg, Fla., Rich volunteers his time and efforts as an executive committee member of his local chapter of the American Diabetes Association. Rich lives in St. Petersburg, Fla with his wife, Jill, and three children, Jason, Lindsey and Bryan.

For more information on Rich Hollenberg, visit **www. richhollenberg.com** or follow him on Twitter **@richonsports**.

KELLI KUEHNE

Kelli is a championship golfer who turned professional in 1998. Born and raised in Texas, Kelli was one of the most successful amateurs of all time, winning three USGA titles including the 1994 US Junior Girls, the 1995 and 1996 US Women's Amateur as well as the 1996 British Amateur—the only golfer in history to have won those events in consecutive years. At the University of Texas, Kelli was a first team All American and was inducted into the Texas Sports Hall of Fame. In addition to winning her first championship in only her second year on tour, she also competed on two US Solheim Cup teams in 2002 and 2003. After turning professional, she won more than $2.2 million in career earnings. Kelli is a spokesperson for the JDRF and she has raised more than $2 million for that organization. She is an advocate for promoting education and awareness for people and families living with diabetes.

Kelli lives in Park City, Utah with her husband, Paul, and daughter, Morgan.

For more information on Kelli Kuehne, visit **www.kellikuehne. com**, **www.playkleen.com** or follow her on Twitter **@kellikuehne**.

TOM KARLYA

Tom has been active in diabetes causes since his daughter, Kaitlyn, was diagnosed in 1992. He is vice president of the Diabetes Research Institute Foundation and volunteers for Diabetes Advocates, LIONS Diabetes Foundation and Children with Diabetes. He writes daily at www.diabetesdad.org and he has written and produced public service announcements for diabetes causes featuring celebrities such as Ray Romano, Sugar Ray Leonard, Doris Roberts, Nicole Johnson (Miss America 1999), Sandra Oh, Patti LaBelle, Peter Boyle, Brett Michaels and Jim Turner. Tom was awarded the Jeff Hitchcock Distinguished Service Award from Children With Diabetes in 2008 and was named Man of the Year by the LI Advertising Club, as well as Diabetes Advocate of the Year by the American Association of Diabetes Educators. As producer of *dLife* TV, he was nominated for an Emmy Award and has won 13 Telly Awards.

He also received numerous commendations, including congratulations from the president of the United States for his work organizing relief efforts for more than 10,000 people with diabetes after Hurricane Katrina. He was the recipient of the George Estabrook Award from his alma mater of Hofstra University for his work in diabetes and television.

For more information on The Diabetes Research Institute; a world leader in cure focused research, visit **www.diabetesresearch. org**. You can also find his daily articles to inspire and educate at **www.diabetesdad.org** or visit him on Twitter **@diabetesdad**.

BARBARA ANDERSON

Barbara J. Anderson, Ph.D, is a behavioral scientist and licensed clinical psychologist with 30 years of experience in diabetes research as well as in clinical work with youth with diabetes and their families. She has published extensively on the complex inter-relationships among emotional factors, family involvement, adherence and medical outcomes in youth with diabetes. Dr. Anderson is a professor of pediatrics, and associate head, section of psychology, in the department of pediatrics, at Baylor College of Medicine in Houston, Texas. Prior to returning home to Texas, Dr. Anderson worked at The Joslin Diabetes Center in Boston.

In 2010, Dr. Anderson received the Education and Advocacy Award from the International Society for Pediatric and Adolescent Diabetes. It was during this international advocacy work where she first learned of the Life For A Child program and continues to be a huge champion for raising the visibility of the program regarding the ongoing challenge for insulin access and diabetes education in developing countries. In 2011, she received the Distinguished Contributions in Behavioral Medicine and Psychology Award from the American Diabetes Association.

For more information on Barbara's publication, "Cowboys and Horse Whisperers: Changing Paradigms of Diabetes Education and Care," visit **www.spectrum.diabetesjournals.org/content/16/4/269.full.pdf+html**. For more information on Life for a Child, visit **www.lifeforachild.org**.

MORGAN PATTON

Morgan Patton is 24 years old and resides in Athens, Ga. She is a professional cyclist with type 1 diabetes and is also in charge of the Team Novo Nordisk Junior Development program. She has had type 1 diabetes since 1995 and been a part of the team since 2007. She has raced successfully at the professional level in women's cycling since 2008. Being a part of the team has changed her from a rebellious teen with an HbA1C in the double digits to a role model of what's possible when you take control of your disease. Her ultimate goal is to empower, inspire and motivate those with diabetes to live their lives to the fullest.

Visit her on Twitter **@morganpatton**.

JEFF HITCHCOCK

Jeff Hitchcock is the president and founder of Children with Diabetes, Inc. (CWD). CWD hosts one of the largest diabetes-related websites in the world at www.childrenwithdiabetes.com. The CWD website typically receives more than 20,000 visitors per day from countries around the world. CWD also hosts educational and support conferences throughout the year, including its national *Friends for Life* conference held annually in Orlando, Fla. Thousands of people from across the U.S. and the world attend.

Jeff founded CWD in June 1995 to share his family's experiences in raising a child with diabetes. Marissa, Jeff and Brenda's first child, was diagnosed in September 1989 at the age of 24 months. She graduated with a Bachelor in Nursing degree from the University of Cincinnati in 2009, was married in 2012, and is expecting her first child.

In March 2008, CWD became part of the Johnson & Johnson family of companies. CWD's mission remains unchanged: to provide unbiased, science-based education and support to families living with type 1 diabetes.

Jeff lives in the Cincinnati area with his wife Brenda, daughter Kathryn, and son, Tim.

For more information on Children With Diabetes, visit **www. childrenwithdiabetes.com** or follow them at **@cwdiabetes**.

DEREK ROWLEY

Derek was diagnosed with diabetes in 2003 at the age of 13. He first became active in diabetes causes as a counselor at Camp Kudzu, a Georgia summer camp for children with diabetes that he originally attended as a camper. In 2012, Derek graduated with academic distinctions from Stanford University with a degree in human biology. Today, Derek lives in San Francisco and works as a business analyst for McKinsey & Company. While at McKinsey, Derek has spent much of his time focusing on strategy and operations work within the medical products and healthcare industries. Derek will be returning to The Stanford Graduate School of Business in 2014 to pursue his MBA.

ROBERT CAMPBELL

Robert W. Campbell Jr. was diagnosed with type 1 diabetes in 1977. Today, he resides in Maine, where he was born and raised. Rob is vice president of innovation and product research at Insulet Corporation and was one of the first employees. He has held various clinical, marketing and product development roles since joining the company in early 2001. He is actively involved in clinical research, international expansion, next-generation product development and alternative applications.

Rob spent many years working at the Elliott P. Joslin Camp for children with diabetes and attributes his passion and focus on helping others with diabetes from this experience.

Rob holds a deep passion for sports, business, the outdoors, the environment, and is dedicated to giving back. He has learned many lessons from business pioneer and environmentalist Yvon Chouinard (founder of Patagonia) and Bill Carlson (first with diabetes to complete an Ironman in 1983). These are two of the many important role models that have encouraged him to follow his dreams and reach for the highest levels of success, type 1 diabetes notwithstanding. He continues to give back and enjoys giving motivational talks at local schools to children of all ages, encouraging them to dream big and foster an "anything is possible" attitude.

He received a Bachelor of Science degree in engineering from Humboldt State University, where he has established a scholarship fund for engineering and nursing students in memory of his late father, Robert W. Campbell Sr.

KAMAAL WASHINGTON

Kamaal Washington is a noted diabetes health advocate, socially-conscious comic book creator and social media crime-fighter. He has been active in fighting crime and drugs in the urban core since he was a child. He is the son of a well-known community activist who battles these social ills on a regular basis. When he was diagnosed with type 1 diabetes at the age of 9, Kamaal published a comic book to teach other kids the signs, symptoms and management of the illness. Along with his brother, Malcolm, they have written several *Omega Boy versus Doctor Diabetes* comics to help explain type 1 diabetes to children and to raise diabetes awareness in youth across America. The effort also includes their national "Tour for a Cure." Kamaal is one of America's youngest comic book publishers in history.

ABOUT THE AUTHOR

Andrew Deutscher is a passionate advocate for type 1 diabetes. He serves on multiple committees for JDRF Georgia, including Government Relations, Walk outreach, Support Group leadership and contacting newly diagnosed families. Andrew is a parent of a type 1 boy, Gavin, diagnosed at 22 months, who is now 6. Andrew is Vice President for The Energy Project and has keynoted and led workshops for well-known corporate brands, including Coca-Cola, Marriott, Twitter, Genentech, Campbell's and many others. His experience speaking on the topic of sustainable high performance in corporations worldwide has enabled him to frame diabetes care in an empowering way and has earned him respect as a trusted resource among peers and other type 1 individuals and families. The stories and information in this book will empower you to keep A1C levels in your loved one moderate and their self-esteem high. Andrew lives in Atlanta, Georgia, with his wife Tara and their two boys, Jake (8) and Gavin (6).